ALEXANDER YAKOVLEV

NOTES OF AN AIRCRAFT DESIGNER

FOREIGN LANGUAGES PUBLISHING HOUSE
MOSCOW

TRANSLATED FROM THE RUSSIAN
BY ALBERT ZDORNYKH

DESIGNED BY ALEXANDER VASIN

Александр Яковлев

РАССКАЗЫ
АВИАКОНСТРУКТОРА

CONTENTS

1*

CHAPTER ONE

FROM A MODEL TO A GLIDER

MY FIRST ENCOUNTER WITH AN AIRPLANE

I saw an airplane for the first time in my life when I was six. I remember it was a holiday and my parents had gone to visit some acquaintances of ours. I was left at home with my grandmother. She always used to cuddle me, but this time she decided to give me an unusual treat :

"We're going to Khodynka to see balloons in the air."

Granny had in mind the kind of observation balloons called aerostats.

It was a long way from the Pokrovsky Bridge to the Petrovsky Park. At last we got by tram to Khodynka. A large, open field, it was already full of people.

I looked at the sky but saw no sign of balloons. I was getting rather bored with the whole thing when I suddenly heard a kind of rattling noise. I pushed to the front and saw a small curious machine that looked more like a bookshelf than a balloon. It was some French airplane, perhaps a Farman or a Blériot. With its wings outspread the airplane rolled clumsily across the field rattling away and scaring the wits out of the inquisitive spectators.

"It's going to fly now!" I heard people exclaim around me. But the airplane turned round, trundled to the other end of the field and came to a stop. Some time passed before it rattled across the field again and then back once more. This was repeated several times. The airplane for some reason could not take off.

That evening we got home late; I felt tired and disappointed. This was my first acquaintance with aviation.

At that time aviation in Russia was in its embryo stage. There were almost no Russian-built airplanes, although by that time Nikolai Zhukovsky, a famous Russian scientist, mathematician and mechanic, had already evolved the theory of flight—aircraft aerodynamics, which to this day is the corner-stone of the world's aviation science, and a group of engineers from the Russko-Baltiisky Plant headed by the designer Igor Sikorsky had created a four-engined *Ilya Muromets*, the largest airplane in the world. The tsarist government considered it much safer to buy the approved foreign designs than run the risk of promoting their own "home-made engineers." Businessmen had no wish to spend money on experiments and research. They preferred to buy airplane parts in France and assemble them in Russia: it was far more profitable that way.

It was in those foreign bookshelf-planes that Russian pilots made their first flights.

The names of such pilots as Pyotr Nesterov, Sergei Utochkin, Boris Rossinsky and other pioneers of the air in Russia were very popular at that time. At Khodynka I witnessed the failure of one of the earlier flying experiments. The plane did not even take off. I was not much impressed, and very soon forgot all about the airplanes and the airfield.

Of course, no one in my family could even think that I would ever become an aircraft designer, although my mother used to say that I should be an engineer. To tell you the truth, for as long as I can remember I had always dreamed of becoming an engineer. Egged on by a desire to see what made them run I ruthlessly gutted all my toys—locomotives, carriages, tram-cars and clock-work motor cars. I was always assembling or taking something apart. Screwdrivers, pliers and cutters were my passion. I felt myself on top of the world when I was given a bit brace.

At nine I decided to be a railway engineer.

My uncle Nikolai Chernevsky, a railway engineer, took me with him for summer vacations to the remote part of the Vetluga forests where he was supervising the building of the Nizhny Novgorod-Kotelnich railway line. For hours I used to sit by the railway bed absorbed in watching the workers lay the rails or span the bridge across the Vetluga River. I was a kid and to me it was all poetry.

At last the first train rolled over the new railway line. The engine moved slowly and cautiously ahead, and the engine-driver kept poking his head out of the cab. Whooping and shouting the workers ran alongside the engine.

My uncle looked bright and happy. Excited and rather nervous he accepted the congratulations which poured in: it was owing to his drawings and under his supervision that this large group of builders—engineers, technicians, workers—had laid the rails through the woods and marshes, spanned rivers and built stations.

Airplanes were far from my thoughts then.

WITH LOVE AND DEVOTION

When I was nine it was time for me to go to school. My parents wanted me to enter the Eleventh Moscow Gymnasium.

I had to take entrance examinations in maths, Russian and Divinity. When I got two excellent and one good mark, I thought I had made it. But to enter the gymnasium all my marks should have been "excellent." The children of landlords and government officials were enrolled with "good" or even "satisfactory" marks. My father was no landlord; he worked for a private oil firm of Nobel Bros. Company in Moscow.

I was taken to a private gymnasium where the entrance rules were less severe. I passed my examinations with the same marks and was enrolled in the preparatory form. I studied at the gymnasium for three years until in 1917 it became a Soviet school.

The private gymnasium for boys where I studied

was one of the best Moscow schools of its kind. A light-yellow three-storey building in Sadovaya-Spasskaya St., it stood off the street behind clumps of spreading jasmine and branching lime and chestnut trees, fenced off by an iron grille. The building itself was notable: it was an addition to a house which had belonged to Mamontov, in his time a well-known philanthropist and patron of arts. The famous Russian singer Fyodor Chaliapin performed for the first time in Mamontov's "private opera" in the Grand Hall which later became our auditorium. In the hall many young painters, Mikhail Vrubel among them, had first shown their skill at stage design.

Today, forty years later, I often drive past the former gymnasium on my way to the Ministry, and every time I look with love and devotion at the windows behind which I spent the years of my childhood and youth. Today the Institute of Printing and Publishing is housed in the building, and past it along Sadovaya Street moves an endless stream of trolley-buses and motor cars. In the days past I remember an endless stream of shadowy characters, tramps and suchlike from the neighbouring Sukharevsky market-place, scurrying past our gymnasium from dusk till night, dray-carts thundering over the cobble-stones, clanking and rattling tram-cars crawling along at a snail's pace with clusters of people clinging to their sides.

Beside our ordinary class-rooms we had special rooms for physics and chemistry equipped with apparatus for tests and experiments, a drawing studio full of stuffed birds and plaster casts of antique sculptures, a gym and a concert hall—called the Chaliapin Hall. The fumed oak wainscot, deep-brown walls and massive wood ceiling gave the hall a solemn and distinguished appearance. The walls above the panelling were lined up with portraits of Russian poets and writers beginning with Mikhail Lomonosov and to our days.

We had a canteen where we were served with *zrazy*—meat pies stuffed with rice and garnished with buckwheat gruel for lunch. We paid for our meals in advance each month, and at lunch time everything was ready and waiting for us. Our teachers had their lunch with us, so we behaved properly at table. Several tables were set aside for those who either did not wish or could not afford the full lunch. There they could have a cup of tea with bread-and-butter or a roll they had brought from home.

Practically all of us were children of intelligentsia. Our marks were also middling. There were no infant prodigies among us, although there were no particular slackers either. As at all other schools there were desks at the back of the room for the dunces. Second-termers—a rare phenomenon with us—also used to sit at the back of the room.

Up in front sat those who had good marks for their studies and behaviour, and naturally there was a shade of coldness between those who sat in front and those who populated the desks at the back of the room.

When our gymnasium became a Soviet school it was amalgamated with a girls' school.

MY FAVOURITE SUBJECTS

During the nine years at school I think I was a willing student. It seems strange to me now, but at that time my favourite subjects were history, geography and literature and not maths, physics and chemistry as would have been more in line with my future profession. I used to get "excellent" for my favourite subjects, while for the latter three my marks were usually "good."

However, this did not prevent me from showing great interest in technology. I participated enthusiastically in various school amateur circles: first in radio, then in aircraft modelling and then in a glider circle. For a time I was the editor of the students' literary and historic journal and even a member of the school dramatic group.

I must say that already in those school years

our inclinations for this or that subject skilfully directed by our instructors in fact decided our future professions. Kostya Vulfson, Yura Protasov, Abram Shirman and other members of our technical amateur circles later became engineers and scientists. Nikolai Chaplygin and Anatoly Ktorov, members of our dramatic group, became actors. Our school helped us future engineers, artists and scientists a great deal in developing our natural talents.

Drawing classes were very well organized at our school. That was one of my favourite subjects too, and my mother encouraged my enthusiasm in every way by making me presents of drawing-books, water-colours and pencils. Later on my experience in drawing helped me a lot in my designing work. When a designer works on a new aircraft, he must be able to put his thoughts, his future creation, on paper in detail.

I AM LEARNING TO ANSWER FOR MY BEHAVIOUR

There are some memories from our school years which we carry all our life. Here are some of mine.

The noon break is just over. The seat next to me on the first desk in the preparatory form is occupied by the nine-year-old Yura Salatko. Our teacher Margarita Yevgrafovna is late.

"I'm a boa constrictor and you're a tiger! Defend yourself!" Salatko cries out and pounces on me strangling and tickling me. Imitating the tiger I struggle free roaring with delight.

We were so carried away with our game that we did not notice Margarita Yevgrafovna enter the room. I can see her now, in her black austere dress with a golden chain round her neck, strict, just and invariably adored by all preparatory form pupils. She was preparatory form mistress for years at school.

"What is this! Get up!" said Margarita Yevgrafovna.

We stood up embarrassed, red and dishevelled.

"It's all his fault," I began tearfully.

"So it's all his fault, and you are not to blame!" said Margarita Yevgrafovna darkly. "Very well, then, take your things and move to the desk at the back. No one will pester you there. You'll sit there until you learn to answer for your own behaviour."

Even now I remember my bitter tears and my humiliation at being transferred from the front desk to the back of the room; I remember how ashamed of myself I felt in front of my friends and the teacher. But it taught me a very good lesson for the rest of my life—never to lay the blame for my own actions on somebody else's shoulders.

Several of the boys, including myself, impressed by the adventures of Tom Sawyer and other adventure stories, began to explore our school building. It was a rather old building. We found a cellar connecting the school with another house. A long passage, gloomy vaults, unexpected side passages reminded us of the catacombs. We decided that they were old secret passages.

We made a thorough examination of the cellar with electric torches in search of hidden treasures or at least human skulls. Naturally there were neither ancient tombs, nor hidden treasures. We talked some pupils from another form into exploring the mysterious underground passages with us. Suddenly out of the darkness a ghost loomed up before them. It was I swathed in a white tablecloth "borrowed" from our canteen. Two green torches shone in place of my eyes. But the effect was spoilt by a girl who became hysterical from fright. We ended at the principal's, our parents were summoned....

In 1919-20 when food was hard to get the students—members of our school economic committee—delivered provision to our canteen themselves. One sunny day in March we were excused from lessons and set out in good spirits with a sledge for the food storehouse near Pokrovsky Boulevard.

We were given a sack of lentils, a box of macaroni, a sack of raisins and some other foodstuffs. We loaded everything on to our sledge and made for the school. The sack of raisins, the most valuable part of the cargo, was entrusted to Turkin, a fifth-former. Talking and laughing animatedly our food caravan reached a pond on Pokrovsky Boulevard. There were no railings around it, and this prompted Turkin to take a short-cut across the pond. He ran down and stepped on the black crumbly snow. Our cries of warning only encouraged him. Turkin in his school uniform greatcoat and cap sang a marching-song and stepping smartly in a military manner marched across the ice carrying the sack of raisins on his shoulder. We stopped in our tracks sensing impending disaster.

Suddenly the ice began to crack and give way. Water spurted up, and our brave Turkin began to sink. "The raisins, the raisins!" we shouted in unison. Cold and pale with fear, Turkin stood neck-deep in the icy water holding the valuable sack high above his head. Fortunately, he had not gone very far from the edge, otherwise our life-saving operation would have been more complicated.

We got the shivering and trembling Turkin out of the pond. Water poured from his greatcoat. But

Ilya Muromets, the first four-engined giant in the world

School modelling group organized by Yakovlev (extreme right) in 1923

except for one of his lost galoshes, he was safe and sound. We burst out laughing at the sight of him and the victim could not keep from laughing either.

Suddenly he became gloomy.

"Boys, how can I go home without my galosh? Mother won't let me in, she'll send me off looking for it."

I did not know how he managed to settle the loss with his mother, but we knew that we had it coming from our principal.

OUR TEACHERS

We had all sorts of teachers, most of them good.

I remember Andrei Kuzmich Golubkov, our maths teacher, who saw us through from the first to the very last year at school. He was a small, neatly dressed old man wearing spectacles, who had to use crutches and moved about slowly and cautiously. He was unhurried and deliberate in everything. We respected Andrei Kuzmich very much and were even a little afraid of him, although he never raised his voice. He would call someone to the blackboard and give him a problem to solve. "I see you haven't prepared your lesson, my boy. That's very bad of you, sir. You've hurt my feelings. What shall we do with you?"

He would take out his little notebook and jot

some mysterious sign down in it. He never gave us any marks. His habit was to decipher the mysterious signs in his sacred notebook and enter our final marks in the class register at the end of the term. Very exacting himself he imparted to us a taste for mathematical order and accuracy in all our notes and solutions of problems which developed into a firm habit. All this came in very handy later in our lives.

Our geography teacher was Victor Oktavianovich Blazheyevich. "By way of introduction," he began in his first lesson, "I shall read to you 'Mapui House' by Jack London."

We listened to the story with bated breath and then to the interesting explanation given by our teacher. He read the story during the whole of the first lesson and finished it after the interval.

He won our hearts immediately and from then onwards we were always impatient for his lessons.

For our history teacher we had Zoya Nikolayevna. She also managed to arouse our interest from the very first lesson when she took us to the History Museum on an excursion. In the museum halls she acted as our guide and gave us very interesting explanations. Her lessons were always fascinating. She used to bring with her specimens of ancient weapons, spearheads, stone axes, primitive man's utensils. Later came a model of an Assyrian temple, a model of the Parthenon. She told us stories about ancient Greece, Rome, Egypt, about Pharaohs and pyramids. We made drawings of pyramids, models of sarcophagi, drew pictures on historical themes and even put out a history journal.

I clearly remember the name and appearance of our psychology teacher—Pyotr Mikhailovich. He used to ride up to the gymnasium in a sleigh, wearing a beaver coat and a perfectly cut suit. I remember even his striped trousers. But there is not a trace in my memory of how and what he taught us. Perhaps, just a Latin phrase he began his first lesson with: "Cogito—ergo sum, dubito—ergo sum" (I think, therefore I am, I doubt, therefore I am).

DO YOU LIKE MUSIC?

Kalistratych, noisy and quarrelsome, with the purple-bluish nose of a drunkard, presided at our singing lessons. He liked to tag the pupils with all sorts of nicknames: "What kind of voice is that? You sing like a teapot with its lid missing." Or: "You smell of dirty rags. Do you ever wash?"

Kalistratych made us learn round songs. We schoolboys could not grasp their meaning and the teacher could not help us at all.

He was only with us for a brief period of time and was then replaced by Anna Nikolayevna, an elderly, stout woman with smiling eyes.

We were already prejudiced against singing lessons and regarded them as a waste of time. However she managed to change our views entirely.

When she first appeared in class, she sat down at the grand piano after greeting us and then turned to a line of thirty imps aged ten to twelve standing in two ranks.

"Well, children, do any of you like music?"

We were silent.

"Do you like music?" she asked the boy on the extreme left.

"No."

She repeated the question to a second boy and a third, and all of them repeated "no." Then Anna Nikolayevna said:

"Listen!" And she played the gay tune of a comic song we all knew.

The boys burst out laughing and, before she had time to finish the tune, cried in unison, " 'Chizhik!' 'Chizhik!' "

"There!" exclaimed Anna Nikolayevna laughing. "It appears that everyone of you is a musician at heart and has an ear for music: you knew it's 'Chizhik' straight away!"

She won our sympathy from the very first meeting, and singing lessons became favourite with us. We sang with great zest such wonderful songs as "Orlyonok" (The Young Eagle), "The Cruiser *Varyag*" and even "On the Hills of Manchuria."

There was not a single lesson at which Anna Nikolayevna did not play some new piece on the grand piano fostering in us a love for good music and for art.

I think that that also left an imprint on me which lasted all my life.

GOOD BOOKS

On one of my birthdays I got two books for a present—*The Adventures of Robinson Crusoe* which I read scores of times, dreaming just as most boys of ten of finding myself a Crusoe on a desert island, and *Stories* by Jack London. I liked his heroes—strong, brave, resourceful and courageous people who were not afraid of dangers and tackled them without a trace of fear. But I especially liked the books which I read after these first two: the animal stories by Ernest Thompson, *Mawgli* by Rudyard Kipling and Mark Twain's books—*The Adventures of Tom Sawyer* and *The Adventures of Huckleberry Finn*. I had learned to read when I was five, but in the gymnasium I took to it in earnest.

At school we had a very good library run by one of our teachers. He knew our tastes and what to recommend to each of us.

I read avidly and was attracted mainly by adventure stories: *The Headless Rider*, *Leather-*

Stocking, The Last of the Mohicans were my favourites. I made the acquaintance of Montigomo the Hawk-Eye, learned about wigwams, pipes of peace and when and how they were smoked.

I learned how cruel the first Spanish colonizers were towards the native Indian tribes, how ruthlessly they exterminated the natives of this rich land.

At eleven I read all of Jules Verne. In his novels reality was closely interwoven with fiction and adventure. These books increased my interest in technology.

My homework done I would sit with a book reading until it was time to go to bed. But I could not tear myself away from the book. That caused me a lot of trouble. My mother would come and take the book away from me saying it was high time for bed. So I had to resort to all sorts of tricks. I would pretend I had fallen asleep and then, when everyone was sleeping, I would turn on the light and read until three or four in the morning. I remember the talkings-to my mother gave me every time she caught me.

MORE BOOKS

I used to spend summer at my uncle's. He had a very large library and subscribed to a couple of magazines with supplements about travels, discoveries and inventions. From these supplements I learned about Przhevalsky, Miklukha-Maklai, Kruzenshtern, Sedov, Bering, Christopher Columbus, Amundsen, Nansen, Livingstone and many other courageous travellers.

The adventures of the characters of the French writers Louis Boussenard and Louis Jacolliot who travelled practically in all the countries of the world gripped my imagination. Reading about the character of different peoples with their customs and ways of life and carried away by the stories I was taken to distant lands where I lived and fought together with my heroes.

Then came books about the father of Russian learning—Mikhail Lomonosov, about Popov, the inventor of radio, about Mendeleyev and about other scientists and inventors.

I read a great many books on Russian history. These fascinated me and planted in me a deep love towards Russia and a pride in my people and their history, their great rulers and generals—Peter the Great, Suvorov, Kutuzov.

Through books I became passionately interested in technology; they taught me to dream, to imagine my future. But they did not only teach me to dream, they called me to deeds, to action. My favourite heroes were daring, industrious and persevering in their aims. They overcame every obstacle. I also dreamed of accomplishing something difficult in life.

PERPETUUM MOBILE

I was twelve when I read about the life of Ivan Kulibin, a famous Russian inventor who thought of developing a perpetual machine—perpetuum mobile. I also decided to invent a perpetual motion machine which once started would work for ever without fuel or power of any sort. And although I learned from the same book that that was an impossible task I nevertheless thought: "What if it comes off?" I drew diagrams and pictures, even tried to build something and, of course, nothing came of it.

After my stay with my uncle at the construction site on the railway I began making models of locomotives, carriages and complicated railway bridges. But very soon I got tired of them. They were dead, mere toys. And I wanted to build something that would really work.

I got interested in radio engineering. At that time there were only a few radio amateurs in Moscow. Radio communications were something of a novelty in those days. Nevertheless, we managed to build a wireless in our school radio circle. Sometimes we would receive a station, but it was not much fun really—you have to sit for hours with earphones on, searching the ether.

Young designer explaining his aircraft to the Pioneers who collected money for building it

Yakovlev's glider in flight (1924)

One day I came across a book of stories about the history of science. There were stories about the invention of railways, the discovery of electricity and the appearance of aviation. The book also contained the description of a model of a glider with a diagram attached to it.

The wireless was forgotten and my room was turned into a workshop. The smell of glue invaded the room and the floor was littered with wood shavings and paper scraps. I had no time either for games or play. For more than a month I was busy building the model of a glider out of thin pine planks covered with paper and fastened together with nails and glue. The glider's wing span was six feet, and naturally could not be tested at home. So I had to disassemble the glider and carry it to school. In our auditorium amidst the solemn silence of a crowd of curious onlookers I launched my first flying apparatus, and it flew about 50 feet.

I was overjoyed. Everyone present in the hall was gripped with excitement. The model flew. I was conscious of its movement, of its life. It was at this exact moment that my passion for aviation was kindled!

Model aviation became the topic of the day at school. Some of my friends contracted "aviation fever." We stayed at school after the lessons and built one model after another. Some of them managed to fly a short distance, others completely failed to stay in the air. One of the models was so big we could not find a hall big enough to test it in. Meanwhile our enthusiasm grew.

FRIENDS OF THE AIR FLEET

It was 1923, my last year at school. The Society of Friends of the Air Fleet—SFAF—was established in the country. We decided to set up a cell of young friends of the Air Fleet at school and organized our model fans into a team.

We had some experience in building and testing models but it was not enough now. We wanted to create something big, to really help in building up our Red Air Fleet.

Five youngsters, friends of the Air Fleet, began to frequent SFAF lectures, begged literature on aviation and eagerly devoured every book we could lay our hands on.

"Give us some real job, some assignment," we kept asking at the society. A campaign for raising funds to build the Air Fleet was underway at that time, and so we got ourselves a job walking the streets with collection boxes slung across our shoulders on belts and persuading Muskovites to give money to build the Air Fleet.

People gave generously, and we brought back full boxes. Our standing as active members of the society was firmly established. Now they could give us more important jobs.

The First All-Russian Agricultural Exhibition was opened in 1923 on the site of the present-day Gorky Recreation Park. There on the bank of the Moskva River by the Krymsky Bridge was an aeroclub where visitors to the exhibition were given paid rides on a Junkers seaplane. We, boys, eager to help the society, volunteered to work at the aeroclub and were taken on.

I worked as a team with one of my school friends, a very funny lad who when introduced, no matter whether to adults or boys of his age, would give his full name and patronymics: Alexander Pavlovich Grishin. He would say it with great self-respect and the air of a worldly-wise, reliable man, although he was a thin, snub-nosed fourteen-year-old lad.

Alexander and I worked hard. Naturally, we took no part in flying and repairing the seaplane. Our job was to maintain order in the queue and sell tickets, but we certainly made everyone understand who were the managers around there. As a reward for our diligence we were allowed near the seaplane and even to wipe some of its parts clean standing knee-deep in the water. That suited us down to the ground. Alexander could not boast of being dexterous: every time he would slip off the plane's float into the river and go home sopping wet. But his face reflected nothing but complete pleasure and delight.

AVIATION BECOMES MY DREAM

Soon we learned that at the Khodynka Field there was a dump of old airplanes that had served their time. After discussing the matter we decided to get a real scrapped aircraft, take it to bits and learn the purpose of each part and how it worked. It fell to our lot, Alexander's and mine, to be the solicitors, as it were, in this affair. Time and again we appeared before the SFAF executives to argue our case, time and again we were refused, but we came again and again and at last we got permission.

With this permission in our pocket we went to the Khodynka Central Aviation Dump for an airplane. We loaded an old half-demolished captured Nieuport on to the cart and walked proudly, with serious faces, in a group down the middle of the street behind our precious load. The winter day was frosty, the horse pulled the cart slowly, but neither of us felt the cold. We were happy: let everybody see our march of triumph.

At last we arrived at the school. When we hauled the airplane into the auditorium, there was a great commotion among the schoolchildren. Everyone looked at it with caution although our aircraft lacked the wings, fin and, of course, armament. Our sceptical-minded assistant director guardedly voiced his opinion: "I hope nothing will blow up."

We felt ourselves heroes of the day, and looked proudly upon everybody and especially at the girls.

It took us much time to disassemble and then to assemble the airplane and to restore damaged parts. We brought the missing wings and fin from the airfield. The airplane, of course, could not be used for flying, but this kind of work did us a lot of good. Together with the rest of the boys I made my first thorough acquaintance with a real aircraft.

Very often we went to the airfield to watch the airplanes fly. We were not allowed on the field without a pass, so we peeked through cracks in the fence and followed the life of the airfield with bated breath. From time to time an airplane would take off. Spellbound, I looked with envy at the helmeted and goggled pilots clad in their leather flying jackets.

Aviation became my dream.

SEEKING ADVICE

At seventeen I finished secondary school and had to choose my future career in earnest. Long before this I had made up my mind to become an aircraft designer. But where to begin, whom to turn to for advice? I knew no one among the airmen.

In the papers I often came across the name of engineer-designer Porokhovshchikov. I don't know how I ever managed to sum up the courage, but I made up my mind to beg him to help me in getting a job in aviation.

In the summer of 1923, not without difficulty, I found Porokhovshchikov at the Main Air Fleet Administration and timidly approached him. He was a tall slender man in a military uniform. I knew he was a busy man and therefore stated my request briefly, but I longed to talk with him about so many things.

"Come to the airfield with me and we will talk on the way."

I readily agreed. How many times I had imagined myself on the airfield while looking through a crack in the fence.

We maintained silence all the way there: I did not know how to start the conversation and the designer was obviously deep in his own thoughts.

When we approached the airfield gates, the

sentry asked sternly: "What about you?"—"He is with me," Porokhovshchikov said to him.

There were no hangars at that time. The planes were parked in the open out on the field. There were several planes captured from the interventionists in the Civil War.

Today these planes would present a pitiful and miserable sight, but at that time I really admired them.

SOME ADVICE. . . .

Porokhovshchikov came to the airfield to examine a new French Caudron machine which had just arrived. I remember the smooth, highly polished ivory sheathing of the wings and tail-plane. But the general impression of the plane was rather strange: it was a chaos of various pipes and wires.

Porokhovshchikov examined the aircraft and went over to another machine. Walking beside him I thought it was the right time to remind him of my presence: "I dream of becoming an engineer. Two years ago I built the model of a glider."

I did not have time to finish. We came up to some old Morane monoplane and Porokhovshchikov launched into conversation with the pilot. Ten minutes later we moved on.

"I attended the aircraft modelling circle," I began once again, "and got very much interested in it. I want to become an aircraft engineer, a designer. I beg you—"

But then we again came to some plane or other and Porokhovshchikov began to examine it, now and then dropping remarks to the mechanic. Seizing an opportunity I continued:

"I would like to get into an aviation school or perhaps you will help me to get a job as mechanic in some flying organization."

Porokhovshchikov listened to me absent-mindedly walking from plane to plane.

At last having finished his inspection he said without looking at me: "Today lots of people want to become designers. It's just a folly. To be a designer is no simple thing. This is not the way to begin."

I was hurt, although I understood perfectly well that Porokhovshchikov had no time for me.

Finally having offered me no explanation as to where the future designer should begin, he told me to go and see some other official. There was nothing I could do. The official heard me out and said:

"Drop in tomorrow."

The next day I heard the same: "Drop in tomorrow."

Alexander Yakovlev, mechanic at the Central Airfield (1925)

Contact!

Then I was told that he was out. I realized I would not get anywhere. I did not want to go to Porokhovshchikov again and so I began to seek other roads to aviation.

MEET YOUR ASSISTANT

In the winter of 1922-23 the newspapers wrote about the first glider competitions to be held in the Crimea in November. I had some idea of how to design a glider and wished to take part in building the first Soviet gliders. I went to Artseulov, then a prominent pilot and aircraft designer who was in charge of the competitions.

Konstantin Konstantinovich Artseulov met me warmly, listened attentively and sympathetically to my story and suggested on the spot:

"Would you like to help Anoshchenko, a pilot, to build a glider of his own design?"

"Of course, I would!" I cried out joyously.

The glidermen worked at the Air Force Academy. I remember a huge unheated hall at the Petrovsky Palace cluttered up with various building materials and glider parts. I was a novice and looked on the glidermen as wizards.

Artseulov took me to a tall man with a kind face: "Nikolai Dmitriyevich, I want you to meet your assistant."

Anoshchenko held out his hand to me:

"How do you do. Glad to meet you! So your name is Alexander. Well, Alexander, let's work together. If you work well we shall take you to the Crimea," he added.

To tell you the truth, I did not believe him then, but I got down to work with great enthusiasm.

I had learned how to handle joiner's tools in my childhood and therefore made good progress. At first Anoshchenko himself spent a lot of time working on the glider, but being one of the organizers of the glider competitions he had plenty of other things to worry about. When he saw the work was turning out well, he appeared at the workshop less frequently. He would come, look at the progress made and give instructions. His confidence flattered me and I strained all my abilities. I was so carried away with my work that I spent whole days at the Academy hall till very late in the evening. My father was displeased with me. He wanted me to get a good job and thought of building a glider as a fool's fancy.

My mother on the contrary defended me. "Let him work for a bit. It's not so bad after all. Maybe, he'll really make an engineer some day."

This was my passionate dream and I hoped it would come true.

The day of the competitions drew nearer, but the glider was not ready yet. I had to work still harder.

Then to my great joy I learned that I was to be sent to the Crimea as a reward for my good work. Anoshchenko and I promised to complete our glider on the spot.

IN THE BOX-CAR

Planernoye, or Koktebel, as it was called in those days, was a summer resort near Feodosia. This corner in the south-east of the Crimea later became the traditional venue for all-Union meetings of the gliding world.

A whole train was assigned to take the participants and their gliders down to the Crimea. We loaded our gliders on flat-cars, covered them with tarpaulins and carried our things to a box-car.

That unusual trip to the Crimea was one of the most vivid impressions in my life. I had never been in the Crimea before, what's more, I had never been anywhere without my mother. Imagine how proud I felt on that first trip on my own. I had official papers in my pocket and some money issued to me by the Administration to cover my daily expenses.

In the box-car among the young aviation enthusiasts Sergei Ilyushin, Vladimir Pyshnov and others, I was in the seventh heaven. Today the whole country knows some of those people. Ilyushin has become a well-known aircraft designer, Pyshnov and Goroshchenko—scientists and professors. In those days they were all students at the Air Force Academy and taking their first steps in aviation.

We had plenty of free time during our journey, for the train dragged on south for six solid days. But the long journey did not seem tedious to me. I learned a lot in the field of aviation and technology, and contact with these wonderful people and good friends gave me moral support for my future work in aviation.

We had left Moscow on a cold bleak day late in the autumn. But as we drew nearer to the south it became warmer and warmer. At last it grew so hot and stuffy in the box-car that we had to move out on to the flat-cars to our gliders. During the day we met in groups and chatted endlessly and at night we returned to our gliders, crawled under the tarpaulin and fell soundly asleep.

One night an unusual and strange sound woke me up. I quickly got up, crawled out from under the tarpaulin, and looked around. Just a few yards away I saw the sea for the first time in my life.

The train had stopped. A full moon was shining in the sky and the silvery sea with the wide moon path running way out to the horizon lay slumbering before me.

We had arrived at Feodosia where the railway station was situated practically on the sea-shore.

The next day we unloaded our gliders from the train and carted them to Koktebel where there was a camp pitched on the hill.

All the gliders had been built in Moscow. They were to be assembled and made ready for flights at the camp. All but ours, which required a lot of finishing touches.

Anoshchenko told me:

"You put in a bit of work here and I'll be off. I have to be at the starting line because I'm on the technical commission, you know."

True, he had to be present for the starts, but imagine how I felt being left alone away from the events.

The competitions had already begun, and while the gliders soared up into the air I was working for all I was worth in the tent. How vexing!

The tent stood more than a mile from the start, and I badly wanted to see the flights. At last I could not restrain myself any longer, dropped everything and ran off to the competitions. Nikolai Dmitriyevich spotted me there and sent me back saying:

"Go on, go on, finish the work and then you'll see everything."

I went back reluctantly. But it was hard to keep my mind on the work, and the next day, taking care to avoid my "boss," I was off again to admire the flights.

Today flocks of Soviet gliders fly hundreds of miles, set up altitude records, accomplish wonderful group flights, perform intricate aerobatics, while in those days only ten machines took part in the First Glider Competitions and no one knew how they would behave in the air. Each designer cherished only one secret wish: if it could only take off. How and where it would fly did not matter, such problems would come later. If it could only take off and land safely.

When the glider designed by Konstantin Artseulov smoothly soared over the starting line, made several small circles and landed safely, the spectators were delighted. They cheered the designer enthusiastically and tossed him into the air several times.

"MACACO"

In two weeks our glider was completed. For some reason or other the designer named it *Macaco.* To tell the truth, I had little hope in our *Macaco* when I saw the other gliders at the competition.

They were all built along the lines of a normal airplane. They had controls, wings, a tail-plane, a fuselage, a pilot's cockpit and a landing gear of the standard aircraft type. Our *Macaco* was most primitive: it had wings and a tail-plane, but there was no cockpit, no controls, no landing gear. The pilot had to carry the glider on his back, take a run and soar into the air balancing the wings with his body.

Our glider looked very much like the one built at the end of the 19th century by Otto Lilienthal, a well-known German gliderman.

Many doubted that our glider could fly at all. All the participants gathered at the starting line and waited impatiently for developments. The brave designer decided to test the *Macaco* himself.

The glider turned out heavier than it had been designed to be: owing to an incorrectly calculated centre of gravity it was tail-heavy. When Nikolai Dmitriyevich put his offspring onto his shoulders and fitted his arms into special grips the tail drooped so heavily that it was impossible to take off. I was instructed to hold the tail up during the take-off run and thus became a "participant" in the first flight.

DECISIVE SECONDS

As a precaution we decided to test our *Macaco* first on a small hillock and not to take off from the hillside as the rest of the gliders did. Anoshchenko selected the place, got ready for the take-off run and waited for a proper gust of wind. I solemnly held up the tail. Suddenly I heard the command: "One, two, three, ready! Let's go!" I clung to the tail and ran for all I was worth. Anoshchenko was a strong, hefty man while I was small and puny. For his every step I had to make three and it was difficult for me to keep the pace and hold up the tail at the same time. At last I heard: "Let go!"

I released the tail, the glider rose up in the air two, six, seven, nine feet, overturned and crashed to the earth.

We all rushed to the wreckage of the glider worried for the pilot's life. But he clambered out of it safe and sound.

Macaco was beyond repair. Now I had plenty of free time and could watch the flights in peace.

What a wonderful sight a soaring glider makes. With its wings outspread the huge white bird circles soundlessly on high.

To those who are used to the flight of roaring airplanes the soaring of a glider seems an incredible thing. These flights without the help of a mechanical engine of any sort, based entirely on the highly perfected machine and the pilot's art made a deep impression on me. Now I became an aviation enthusiast. The choice was made once and for all.

The *Macaco* glider rose up in the air two, six, seven, nine feet, overturned and crashed to the earth

Sports hydroplanes took off from the Moskva River in the heart of the city

At Koktebel I decided to build a real glider all by myself. I had already built models and had studied various glider designs, but I felt that I could not cope with such a difficult task without technical knowledge.

I had to ask someone for advice. I picked out Sergei Ilyushin with whom I had got acquainted on our way to the competition. Ilyushin approved of my idea, but warned me:

"It is not enough just to wish. You must have knowledge besides. Only then can you design gliders correctly. I can help you a lot, of course, with calculations and drawings, but that will be of little use to you. If you work yourself I'll help with advice and explain the most difficult things."

Ilyushin gave me his notes on airplane design and airworthiness and drew out a list of books for me to read. I diligently read all of them and got down to designing the glider. When snags occurred I went to Ilyushin.

Sergei Ilyushin, his wife and their little daughter lived in those days in a small cramped room at the Air Force Academy hostel in the Furmanny Lane. They were always very kind and friendly to me. Ilyushin was studying at the Academy and had little time to spare, nevertheless he would willingly help me with my studies, sometimes for hours on end. There were times when we sat working late into the night.

This was my first technical schooling.

BACK AT SCHOOL

When, with Ilyushin's help, I had finished all the calculations and drawings for the glider, I was faced with the problem where and with whom to build it.

Then I remembered my school and thought I could organize a group there to build the glider.

I went to the school and the first boy I talked to about the glider was a slim, timid but industrious and persevering lad with a funny name Gushcha. I knew him to be a most devoted friend of the Air Fleet.

I told him the reason for my visit. Gushcha heard me out with a serious air and asked me in a business-like manner:

"Shall we build a real glider or just fool around?"

"Of course, a real one. And besides we shall go to the Crimea, for glider competitions." Then I added recalling Anoshchenko's promise:

"If you work well you will also go to the Crimea."

Gushcha grinned distrustfully: "Go on, stop fibbing."

And although he was not sure he would go to the competition he worked with zeal. He and Alexander Grishin who was still attending classes became enthusiastic over glider building.

ROMANCE OF YOUTH

Fifteen schoolboys joined our group and the work went on swimmingly. We met after lessons and planed, glued, sawed and hammered away.

The material came from an aircraft plant and we made ourselves all the parts down to the very smallest. We were working on our glider in the hall, and that brought a steady stream of visitors —boys and girls from the school. Some would make fun of us saying nothing would come out of our idea. But most of the crowd were sympathetic, especially when they began to discern the outlines of a glider. True, it was a shapeless structure at the beginning, just a pile of lathes, planks and wire.

The work which was practically finished came to a halt when we had to cover the glider frame with fabric. Our boys did not know how to sew.

"We shall have to ask the girls," said Gushcha.

Some of the girls readily agreed to help us and soon their deft hands sheathed the glider frame with percale.

During the school term everyone worked in the evening willingly, but then the summer holidays came and our group began to dwindle. The boys went to Pioneer camps and to the country. When we were finishing off the work only five of us remained—five most devoted aircraft enthusiasts. There was little time left, and to get the glider ready for the competitions we had to work day and night.

At last the day when everything was ready arrived. A special commission issued a positive verdict: our glider was accepted for the competition. Now I had to take care of my assistants who deserved the trip to the Crimea. I managed to obtain credentials for Gushcha and Grishin for the Second All-Union Competitions in Koktebel. I knew how they felt because I had experienced the same feelings a year before.

We loaded our treasure on to the flat-car, covered it with a tarpaulin and the glider train set out to the Crimea. This time the trip seemed as if it would never end. At last we arrived at Koktebel.

Our glider took us two days to assemble and then it was placed among the others in one of the aircraft tents on the Uzun-Syrt Hill.

The fabric of the gliders had been doped and the air in the tent was heavy with the heady aroma of a manicure salon.

On the first clear breezy day our glider was brought to the starting line. The technical control commission made a final inspection. The pilot climbed into the cockpit and strapped himself to the seat. Rubber slings were hitched on and the starting crew took their places.

Attention! The controller raised his flag and with the first gust of air waved the craft aloft. The glider rolled slowly along, then lifted its tail and breaking contact with the ground gained altitude. Happy and excited, we watched the creation of our hands soaring up in the air and then sliding down noiselessly to the foot of the hill.

The pilot was satisfied with our machine. It readily responded to the controls and the stability was good. After that it went up practically every day. The design was approved and we received a reward: two hundred rubles and a diploma. This success inspired us.

Our work on the glider left an imprint on Gushcha. He also became a life-long aircraft enthusiast. I met him a few years later and he was already a pilot in the Air Force.

A year passed. I built another glider and then began to design airplanes.

I BECOME A WORKMAN

After our success in Koktebel I dreamed of getting special education but I failed to enter the Zhukovsky Air Force Academy, the only higher aeronautical educational establishment in the country. I lacked the necessary army service record. So I decided to start in aviation from scratch and to get myself a job as a hand at the aircraft workshops.

Some of my school friends did not approve of my decision.

"If you can't enter the Academy," Kolya Roshchin said, "go in for the entrance exams at some other institute. The main thing is not to lose time, you won't catch up later on."

But I could not go against my heart's desire, I could not betray my favourite—aviation. I could not picture myself being a doctor, say, or a schoolteacher.

Hard as I tried I was unable to get a job at the aircraft workshops straight after graduating from school. I went to the Labour Exchange in Rakhmanovsky Lane, now occupied by the Ministry of Public Health, and was registered as an unemployed. I asked them to send me to any factory with a vacancy, planning to shift to an aircraft job at the first opportunity.

However, getting a permanent job in those days was a tough problem. The country was just beginning to get on its feet after the Civil War. The old factories had already been put back into service but the new ones were yet to be built. Unemployed youths crowded the Labour Exchange. More than once we young men and women were given the job of unloading freight wagons of lumber, bricks or potatoes.

I remember a cold and windy day when I was sent to unload potatoes for the first time. The train stood a long way out of the station in the freight yards of the Yaroslavskaya Railway. At first we did not know how to go about unloading the train and the work met with various snags. We had to wheel the wagon ourselves to the unloading ramp and carry the potatoes into the warehouse. But in the end we got the knack of it. Our spirited youthful songs and banter won the day, and the work went on smoothly. And the taste of potatoes boiled in their skins—how delicious it was! We ate them with relish. It was already dark when we finished our work. I was unaccustomed to heavy physical labour and felt very tired but I was cheerful and like the rest of us was satisfied with the day's work.

Time and again I was sent on temporary work and then at last, in March 1924, Ilyushin helped me to get a job at the Air Force Academy training shops.

The workers in the joiner's shop where I got the job scowled and treated me with distrust. Imagine a lad from "the intellectuals" who had graduated from school carrying a plywood box on his back filled with sawdust and pinewood shavings from the jointing machine and the circular saw from morning till night. Surely he had no business to be there. In those years education was not universal and practically everyone who had managed to finish school strove to get into an institute.

There was plenty of work for me. I would carry off the box only to come back and fetch a fresh pile of fragrant resinous shavings from near the machine. This work was usually done by unskilled lads fresh from the village.

At first they avoided calling me by my first name or referring to me as "comrade." They used to call me vaguely "young man." I sensed the pointed scoffing remarks made by workers behind my back, especially when I passed the smoking-room, where five or six men who came for a cigarette break used to sit in clouds of smoke round the drinking-water tank. But I did not feel embarrassed. Soon they saw I was no refined gentleman and that I did not shun work of any kind but carried it out conscientiously and without complaint.

They often saw me with a broom in my hands or lugging heavy steel blanks from the store-room to the machine shop. My hands were all thumbs at first, covered with sores and often bandaged, but that came in very useful later on. I began to get a knowledge of the life of the workshops as it really was.

The attitude of my workmates towards me gradually began to change and finally I became one of the gang.

My work as an unskilled labourer never put me off: fetch that, hold on here, take this away. I was attentive and patient in learning everything around me. Gradually I mastered the art of sharpening cutting tools, of fixing a part in the chuck, of handling a welder's torch. In two years I got acquainted with basic production processes and mastered some of them myself.

After two years of work in the workshops I managed at last to become one of the airfield crew; by this time I already knew what hard work meant.

AT THE CENTRAL AIRFIELD

The Moscow Central Airfield in 1925-26 was not quite the same as it is today. There were no take-off and landing concrete runways, they were not needed by the planes of those days.

A number of wooden hangars stood at the edge of the airfield. One of these belonged to our crew; the neighbouring hangar belonged to the Soviet-German Company Deruluft. Further down stood hangars where R-1 airplanes were assembled at the former Moscow bicycle factory Dux, and the last in the row was the hangar of the Moscow Air Force School.

To the east the airfield was bounded by the military depot and the Aviarabotnik Plant where I used to go begging for glider parts and materials, to the north it was hemmed in by the Leningradsky Prospekt, to the west, by a ravine which served as a graveyard for wrecked airplanes and to the south, by the cemetery for pilots, victims of air crashes.

Flights at the airfield were few and far between as there were not enough planes and those there were could only fly in good weather. The famous Deruluft pilots Shibanov and Bobkov who flew Fokker-3 passenger planes on the regular Moscow-Königsberg line in any weather, were an exception. They were always on time and we used to say we could set our watches by their flights.

The work at the airfield was not very difficult. I was a "hangar-keeper" and my duty was to keep it clean and in proper order, to open it in the morning and lock it up at night; this meant being the first to come in the morning and leaving after everyone had gone at night. My immediate superior was Alexei Demeshkevich, chief squadron engineer, a short, stout, good-natured man who was called Batya* to his face as well as behind his back. When he saw that I carried out my duties conscientiously and showed a considerable interest in airplanes he soon shifted me to the job of junior mechanic.

HELMET WITH A BLUE STAR

At last I had attained my goal—from morning till night with my chief Volodya Korolko, the senior mechanic, I could tinker about with our Ansaldo biplane.

There were three types of planes in the squadron: four Soviet-made R-1 biplanes, four Italian Ansaldo biplanes and several Avro-type machines, modelled on capture trainers, produced by the Leningrad Red Pilot Plant and nicknamed Avrushka. In good flying weather we wheeled the machines out of the hangars, lined them up, filled the petrol tanks, tested the engines and waited for the pilots, students of the Air Force Academy, to come.

Our squadron commander, with whom I was destined to work for a long time to come, was Yulian Piontkovsky.

---

* Dad.—*Tr.*

Piontkovsky, Chernyaev, the squadron commissar, and Demeshkevich, the chief engineer, were the life and soul of our squadron. They were all in love with aviation and brought us, their subordinates, up in the same spirit. Piontkovsky gave the commissar lessons in flying and very soon he began to fly solo.

Yulian Piontkovsky was a fine pilot and a great engineering enthusiast who could turn his hand to anything. Very often we would see our commander standing at the vice in the workshop with his sleeves rolled up turning some part with the skill of a locksmith.

His bicycle and later the Harley Davidson motor cycle he was given as a bonus and still later his GAZ motor car sparkled with cleanliness and were always fitted with some gadget or other of his own invention.

Piontkovsky would very often take me up for a ride. On one occasion after showing off some aerobatics he brought me down practically unconscious.

At the beginning some of my workmates in the squadron used to snub me since they thought of me as just another mother's darling. But very soon my hard work and obvious enthusiasm put me on the same footing as everybody else. In appearance, too, I could not be distinguished from the rest of the crowd. Three years later, at a gathering of pupils from my form which had met to celebrate our school-days and see how each of us was getting on in life, no one recognized me in the sun-tanned soldier they saw, with his top-boots, trench coat and helmet with a blue Air Force star.

CONTACT!

The work at the airfield, though long and strenuous, was full of romance. There was no mechanization of any kind at that time and we had to do everything by hand.

The Ansaldo plane was powered by a very whimsical 300 h.p. Fiat engine. Volodya Korolko and I spent long hours adjusting the engine, but all the same it often conked out immediately after landing. The pilots clambered out of the cockpits and trudged off while we waited for the Red Army men who had been sent to help us. The Ansaldo's tail was like a ton of bricks, for its skid it had an ordinary motor-car spring, so we needed a lot of people.

"Under the tail! Take hold!" Volodya ordered and four people myself included raised the tail to our shoulders. Eight others strained against the wings.

"Heave, ho!"

We often had to wheel the plane, tail first, for a mile or so. This was all right in summer, but in winter the airfield was not cleared of snow, the planes took off and landed on skis; there were no tractors, and so we had to haul the airplane over the snow.

Starting the engine in those days was also no joke, especially when it came to Ansaldo's. You had first to turn the propeller several times and inject some petrol through the valves. Then came the main operation:

"Contact!" I would cry out, grabbing hold of a propeller blade.

"Contact!" Volodya would shout back from the cockpit switching on the engine and spinning the magneto.

I would give a violent jerk to the blade while my assistant jerked the other blades. The screw would make a half-turn. And so it would go on, me, and my assistant, chanting "contact" and turning the screw until the engine fired, belched white smoke and, after warming up, blue tongues of flame danced at the exhaust pipe ends.

FUELLING BELOW ZERO

The petrol was carted to the airfield in cans, and in winter the cans were brought in sleighs. We used to pour the petrol into pails and then climb the ladder, and fill the plane's tanks through funnels with chamois leather filters. Then we would haul a sleigh with a small hot water tank mounted on it up to the plane and pour buckets of water into the radiator. We heated the oil on the stove until it boiled and then carried it across the wind-swept, snow-bound field to prime the airplane.

You cannot imagine how much effort we put into washing the oil off an iced-up airplane tail. I would soak a piece of rag in a half-pail of petrol and set to rubbing the sheathing of the tail. My hands would go numb from the frost and turn white from the evaporating petrol, but I could not stop until we had finished the job and Volodya had taken the sparking plugs out and I had washed them in petrol, and until we had put each and every fault detected by the pilot right, otherwise our Batya would never accept the airplane.

It was no easy job either to haul the machine into the hangar. The skis got stuck on the concrete floor and we had to pile snow on it, only then did we push the hooded plane into its place ready for next day's flights.

During a break it was a pleasure to crowd inside a warm mechanics' hut. A dozen of us would sit smoking round the red-hot iron stove joking, laughing, listening to the stories of the old-timers. Fifteen minutes would fly past unnoticed and then once more we had to go outside into the cold and wind of the airfield.

Soviet aviation was growing its wings at that

time and I witnessed the first historical flights of the planes designed by Polikarpov and Tupolev.

At the airfield to this day there stands a small two-storey pavilion with a tower on its roof flying a striped wind-sleeve.

The pavilion was occupied by the Central Airfield administration and its chief. Each time new planes were tested or some exceptional event occurred in our life at the airfield the small figure of our chief, dressed in a smart uniform, appeared on the balcony of the pavilion. Zinovy Raivicher or Zinochka, as we used to call him among ourselves, would cast an attentive eye over his kingdom and nothing, however small, escaped his keen eye.

Zinovy Raivicher was a great help to me and Piontkovsky in designing and testing new airplanes. He was a true aircraft enthusiast and a good friend.

CHAPTER TWO

FROM A GLIDER TO AN AIRPLANE

AIRPLANES' GRAVEYARD

The success with the glider made me the happiest lad in Moscow, but after seeing the creation of my own hands in the air I had no more peace. I wanted to build a real plane immediately. I decided to develop an aviette—a single-seat winged motor cycle with an 18 h.p. engine.

This time I sought advice from Vladimir Pyshnov who like Ilyushin had taken part in the First Glider Competitions at Koktebel. Both of them were studying at the Air Force Academy and had spent a lot of time with me when I was building my glider. At that time Vladimir was already a real expert in aerodynamics. He suggested that I should build a two-seat aviette with a more powerful engine. "We need this type of plane for training flights far more than a single-seat version," he said. I could not but agree with him.

Having pondered over the preliminary problems I finally got down to designing a two-seat aviette powered by a 60 h.p. engine.

The job turned out to be far more serious and complicated than building a glider. I had to learn the fundamentals of aircraft theory, calculations of airworthiness, the structural resistance of materials and a host of other sciences. I followed the latest achievements in aircraft building in magazines, went to the aircraft plants whenever I had a chance and studied production processes.

It was at this time that I made the acquaintance of the airplane graveyard.

In those days a ravine filled with wrecked airplanes occupied the place where today the Moscow Air Terminal receives planes arriving from all over the world. In the course of a dozen years the ravine had become piled high with the frames of hundreds of planes of various types either captured or made in Russia that had come to grief and were beyond repairs.

I rummaged about among the wrecks with great enthusiasm, not so much hunting for parts for my aviette, as studying the designs of the various planes.

It was a regular, though rather original school for me, a budding aircraft designer. I rummaged about among the wrecked planes examining the nature of break-downs, trying to understand what had caused them and to discover the weak points in damaged parts.

GOOD- AND ILL-WISHERS

It took me nearly a year to make my calculations and draw up the aviette blueprints. When all the preliminary work was completed and the design approved by the Osoaviakhim* technical commission money collected by Moscow Pioneers were allotted to me for building my plane.

The aviette was built by my friends in the squadron, the mechanics headed by Demeshkevich and foremen from the aircraft plant.

It took us eight months to complete the job. We had to build it in our free time and at the end I was utterly exhausted. After a day's work at the airfield I worked from five in the afternoon till eleven in the evening on the aviette, doing the job

* The All-Union Voluntary Society for Support of the Air Force.—*Tr.*

of a designer, treasurer and administrator at the same time. But no matter how exhausted I was it gave me a great feeling of satisfaction.

In every new undertaking when there is a certain amount of risk in it, you always get good- and ill-wishers. My good-wishers, my friends Pyshnov, Ilyushin and others backed me up with their experience and cheerful words. However there were some ill-wishers, too, who tried to interfere with my work and make me lose confidence in myself.

One of the students at the Academy handed in a report to the effect that he thought I had made a mistake when calculating some part of the wing attachment unit and that it would collapse in flight. To this day I can't imagine why he decided to "expose" me without saying a word to me in person. I was summoned by the Osoaviakhim executives and was given a regular examination on aircraft airworthiness.

I felt discouraged. Doubts assailed me and I began to lose confidence in the airworthiness of my aviette. "Perhaps, he is right, this finals student, perhaps he knows what he is talking about," I thought.

I went to Pyshnov who went over my calculations, carefully studied every detail of the design and gave me a written certificate that he guaranteed the airworthiness of the airplane. That decided the fate of my aviette: I was given permission to continue the work.

By May 1, 1927 the airplane was completed and brought to the airfield where a test flight was scheduled for May 12.

SHE'S OFF

That day the airfield was crowded. The aviette with its white freshly varnished body made a favourable impression upon everyone present there. It was so light and bird-like that no one doubted it would fly.

Piontkovsky climbed into the pilot's cockpit. The decisive moment for the airplane and for me was approaching. After testing the engine for a few minutes Piontkovsky made a few runs over the airfield to check how it responded to the controls and then taxied to the start. The controller waved the aviette off.

Full throttle! The airplane started to move and then gently took off. It climbed higher and higher. The pilot circled over the airfield several times and brought the airplane down to land.

Everybody congratulated me, shook hands with me and wished me further success. I felt that I had passed the first test in the art of aircraft designing. It was the happiest day in my life.

THE REWARD

After the first flight the airplane was run through its paces for speed and altitude for another two weeks. It behaved nicely throughout the tests.

The Osoaviakhim commission on long-range flights under Kamenev approved our suggestion that a trial flight along the Moscow-Kharkov-Sevastopol-Moscow route should be organized for the new airplane. I was to take part in the flight myself as a passenger. In the early morning of June 12, 1927 Piontkovsky and I took off from Moscow.

You cannot compare any other rewards with the feeling of satisfaction which you experience way up in the air flying in a plane which is the creation of your own thought down to the last nut and bolt.

After landing and refuelling in Kharkov we touched down in Sevastopol in the evening of the same day.

The return leg of the flight was made by Piontkovsky alone. We installed a spare fuel tank in the passenger seat, and Piontkovsky took off early in the morning from Sevastopol and flew non-stop for fifteen hours and thirty minutes to land in Moscow the same evening.

The flight gave birth to two world records for sports airplanes: the non-stop flight distance

We built our airplane in the laboratory building of the Zhukovsky Air Force Academy

Piontkovsky, the pilot, and Demeshkevich, the flight engineer, captured first place in the flight of sports machines (1935)

(1,420 km.) and the time of being airborne (15 hours 30 minutes). We were given money rewards and diplomas. But the biggest reward of all was the news that I had been accepted by the Air Force Academy for having made a reliable design for an aircraft.

THE ACADEMY

I came to the Air Force Academy not as a boy just out of school, but as a grown-up man with life experience, although not very extensive, as one who had worked in the aircraft workshops and at the airfield for four years. I was not sorry that I had not entered the Academy immediately after school and received my graduation diploma four years later than some of my school friends. What I gained was the experience of working in a collective, and when I became an engineer I knew not only how to design some aircraft or other, but I could also make the parts on a joiner's bench or turn them up in a machine and I knew how they would function in the airplane. To my mind every engineer should go through such a school in his own field. Before the Revolution railway engineers after graduating from the institute had to do a lot of practical work on the locomotives as stokers and then as engine-drivers. Their work was not easier than ours at the airfield. That, in my opinion, is the correct approach.

We had no specialized subjects at the first few terms and studied general mathematics, physics and mechanics. But aircraft designing took such a firm grip on me that I continued to work on new designs apart from the work I had to do at the Academy.

During my first year at the Academy I designed a new low-powered plane mounted on floats. This plane was taken to the Gorky Recreation Park where it took off from and landed on the Moskva River.

While in my second year I built yet another airplane which differed considerably from the previous machines which were biplanes; the latest one was a monoplane. It was also built at an aircraft factory out of the money allotted by the Osoaviakhim.

The monoplane was completed and flight-tested at the airfield in 1929. The design was a success and my friends Filin and Kovalkov, students at the Academy, made a non-stop flight from Moscow to Mineralniye Vody. This was quite an achievement in those days.

In my last year I designed a four-seat passenger plane or "aeromobile" which was completed after I graduated from the Academy.

GRADUATION CEREMONY AT THE KREMLIN

In our third and fourth years we were given lectures in aircraft building techniques, aerodynamics, the calculation of airworthiness, internal combustion engines and a number of other subjects. My studies at the Academy became more interesting since the subjects were directly connected with the designing and building of aircraft which was near and dear to me. The instructors gave me problems to solve and designs to draw in connection with the planes I was working on. Thus, if we had a test in calculating aircraft airworthiness I would hand in the airworthiness calculations of my airplane.

At the Academy I met my first teacher Vladimir Pyshnov who was by then a lecturer on the theory of aerodynamics. Attentive as before he helped me a lot in my work.

In April 1931, I graduated from the Academy. The graduation ceremony was held in the Kremlin and I clearly remember the events of that significant day.

We walked into the Grand Kremlin Palace, went up the wide marble stairway and entered the huge white Georgiyevsky Hall, sparkling and shining with myriads of lights. We were lined up in two rows.

Kliment Voroshilov, then the People's Commissar of Army and Navy, greeted us. We responded loudly and in unison. The graduation order was read out to us complete with our names and ranks in the hushed hall. Then Mikhail Kalinin, the Chairman of the Central Executive Committee of the U.S.S.R., congratulated us upon graduating from the Academy and becoming members of the large family of Red Army commanders. We gave vent to our strained attention in a long enthusiastic "hurrah." Then we were invited to a table laid out in the adjoining hall which seemed just as solemn, with its gilded ornaments and fixtures, as the first hall had.

We took our places and greeted the appearance in the hall of the leaders of our Party and the Government with stormy applause; we spent the rest of this wonderful evening with them.

As I walked home from the Kremlin it seemed to me I had grown wings: the years of study were behind and creative work lay ahead.

NEW PLANS

After graduating from the Academy I was sent to work at one of the Moscow aircraft plants where a group of designers headed by Grigorovich and Polikarpov were working on a new machine. It was an I-5 fighter, the world's fastest airplane of its day, capable of doing 280 k.p.h. The plane was considered to be the latest word in aircraft engineering.

I examined the new fighter and pondered for a long time over its design, and although it appealed to me I came to the conclusion that a faster machine could be built powered by the same 480 h.p. engine.

The I-5 was a biplane and hence had a greater drag as compared with a monoplane in which I thought a higher performance could be obtained using the same type of engine.

This was an entirely new line of thought in combat aviation where only biplanes were used in those days.

I had some experience in designing work and quickly drew out comparable calculations for a monoplane and a biplane powered by the same engine. It turned out that by building a monoplane not only could greater speed be attained, but it could also be made a two-seater.

To make sure my conclusions were not wrong I consulted the specialists. Everything was all right.

Having worked out the design of the plane on paper I proved to the technical commission that a two-seater monoplane powered by a 480 h.p. engine would reach the speed of 320 k.p.h. Though my new project was met by some with disapproval and even animosity it won the day and the Osoaviakhim came through with funds for the construction of the plane. My dream of creating a high-speed aircraft entirely new in design for our Air Force very soon got hold of my assistants.

We formed a small, but tightly knit group of young engineers and workers, prepared the drawings and got down to work. True, we had to work in rather primitive conditions. To begin with we were refused the necessary premises and equipment on the grounds that the construction of our airplane had not been included in the annual production plan of the plant. But the Party organization at the plant got interested in our work and soon with the help of its secretary Fyodor Bashin we managed to get a small room all to ourselves. But the main thing was that all the shops of the plant were always ready to give us a helping hand.

YULIAN PIONTKOVSKY, THE TEST PILOT

Towards the end of the summer of 1932, the airplane made its appearance at the airfield to be taken up by our chief test pilot Yulian Piontkovsky, highly qualified and a wonderful pilot. Courageous but at the same time cautious, he was usually calm before the flight, his confidence worked miracles on the designer.

Piontkovsky and I came to an understanding that if there was some mishap, even the slightest, or if he saw that the plane's behaviour was in any way abnormal he would land immediately without the traditional circle over the airfield.

We agreed to test the machine early one Sunday morning, so as not to draw an inquisitive crowd.

At the appointed time those few who were to be present at the first test flight gathered at the airfield. I gripped Piontkovsky's hand and stepped aside.

The pilot climbed into the front cockpit; in the rear cockpit a load of eighty kilograms was strapped to the passenger seat.

Piontkovsky started up the engine and tested it thoroughly. Then he taxied about the airfield, made a few runs, broke contact with the ground and covered about a mile flying two or three metres above the ground, then landed again and taxied over to the starting line.

"Everything is all right. Request permission to take off."

I waved him off. The pilot pushed the throttle wide open. The engine roared and the airplane streaked forward and rapidly became airborne. We watched its flight with bated breath. Having climbed to about three hundred metres the airplane made a turn and circled over the airfield once, twice.... And with every circle my heart became lighter, everything was all right, indeed.

Finally the airplane came down to land. We ran out to meet it whooping with delight and admiration. Piontkovsky thrust his head out of the cockpit and made a thumb-up sign: excellent! When he jumped down from the plane we rushed to him and tossed him up into the air a few times. That's how test flights usually end, if everything goes smoothly, of course.

"Now tell me straight what you think of the airplane," I said to Piontkovsky afterwards.

"Excellent machine! I don't doubt it can do more than 300," he answered.

EVERYTHING WAS ALL RIGHT

I was very glad to hear that and decided to go up myself and check the speed.

The next day we took off. "Give it the gun!" I told him. Yulian climbed up, levelled the aircraft and shouted back: "Watch her go!"

My eyes were glued to the speed indicator. I saw the needle creeping from 190 to 200 . . . 240 . . . 250 . . . 270 . . . 290 . . . 300. . . . "Now it will stop," thought I. But no, the needle went on reading 310 . . . 320 . . . 330 . . . and finally stopped there. I was proud and excited. My plane had shown a speed of 330 k.p.h.! In other words, it was one of the fastest planes in the world.

The plane appeared at the airfield towards the end of the summer of 1932

Flying schools and aeroclubs received many thousands of UT-2 trainers

I shifted my gaze from the airspeed indicator and watched the behaviour of different parts of the plane at a speed which was unprecedented for that period. Everything seemed to be all right, there were no signs of vibration, no suspicious sounds. The engine ran powerfully with a clean exhaust pitch. All the calculations and forecasts lived up to our expectations: the monoplane showed striking advantages compared with a biplane.

At that moment Piontkovsky turned his wonderful smiling face to me, and I was so happy, that I felt like hugging him there and then.

We landed safely and clambered out of the airplane feeling like world speed champions.

THE AIRPLANE VANISHED

The first flight of the airplane made a tremendous impression among aviation experts. The Air Force Command wished to see our airplane in flight.

That day the weather was bad with a thin drizzle sifting from the sky. When the military came we could not decide for a long time whether to proceed with flights or not. Finally it was agreed to go ahead.

Piontkovsky took his place in the cockpit and tested the engine. His passenger in the rear seat was Lev Malinovsky, the Osoaviakhim Deputy Chairman, a great aviation enthusiast and a charming person who helped us a lot in our work.

After a short run the airplane took off easily, climbed to 150-200 metres, made a turn over the Petrovsky Park and streaked low above the impressed spectators. My tension mounted.

Suddenly near the airfield's southern boundary, somewhere over Khoroshevo, a gleaming strip separated from the plane, the machine began to descend gradually but without losing speed and disappeared beyond the trees. The spinning strip slowly fluttered down to the ground.

WHAT HAPPENED?

I was shaken. The plane should have done another two or three circles over the airfield and then landed, but it had suddenly disappeared. Questions came from all sides: "What has happened? Where is the plane?" But I could not utter a word. I just stood waiting for the machine to pop into sight from behind the trees. "Perhaps it was all a joke the pilot has been playing on us," I thought. But there was not a trace of the plane in the sky. Then we all rushed to the cars and sped along the road in the direction in which the airplane had disappeared. On the way we learned that it had landed somewhere beyond the Vagankovskoye Cemetery near the freight yard.

I was shaking all over. Fear for the pilot and the passenger weighed like a heavy burden on my conscience. When we arrived at the place of the accident, a sigh of relief escaped us all: the pilot and the passenger were alive and the plane intact. It stood on a tiny strip of land in the freight yard clattered with firewood and all sort of rubbish. We found neither Piontkovsky nor his passenger by the airplane. They were gone and the machine was guarded by a militia man. What after all had happened?

I went up to the airplane and discovered that an aileron had torn out of the starboard wing and the damaged sheathing hung in shreds. The aileron had been wrenched out in flight and we had seen it fluttering to the ground.

Brilliant handling of the machine which was practically out of control and a miraculous landing on a tiny strip had averted imminent disaster.

YES, IT WAS A MISTAKE

The airplane was disassembled and brought to the plant where we made a detailed study of the damage. It turned out that the break-down was due to an error made in the calculations of the plane's design. Yes, it was a mistake. We had achieved a tremendous advance in speed in our plane. Particular attention to the aileron wing attachment was therefore required.

A commission was set up to investigate the accident which did not find it necessary to discuss anything with me, and only later did I learn of its verdict, which read as follows: "To forbid Yakovlev to carry on with his designing work and notify the Government that Yakovlev is unworthy of an award" (by that time my name had been put forward for a decoration).

The conclusion of the commission was harsh and unjust. It failed to evaluate the plane and to take into account that it was a novelty for the Soviet Air Force. People began to look askance and even with mistrust at me and at the designers and technicians I had worked with.

Soon after the accident our group was told to clear out of the main factory building immediately. We had to move from the shop into a wooden shed. We put the place in order and began to work there until one day a superintendant came in and said:

"Listen here. There's been an order to keep you off the plant premises and to take away all your passes."

"What shall we do?" I asked him.

"That's no business of mine. Director's orders. So, that's that. Go and look for other jobs."

Things looked tough for us. What was to be done? The director of the plant refused to listen to me and I went for help to the plant's public organizations. The secretary of the factory Komsomol group Sasha Voropanov was the first on my list. He listened attentively to everything I had to say, thought it over and said, "You know, old man, let's go to the Party committee."

Everyone at the plant knew Fyodor Bashin, our Party secretary, to be serious, just and a person of ready sympathy. I had known him since the time he had worked as a joiner at the shop and helped me to build my first sports airplane.

Fyodor Bashin was sitting at the table smoking and listening attentively to a couple of workers holding forth. After they had finished he picked up the receiver and dialled a number. Their request satisfied the workers took their leave.

"I know why you've come to see me, my boy. I'll tell you frankly, the director is a stubborn man. If he doesn't want to help nothing can budge him. He's got powerful support at the top. They won't quarrel with him because of you. But we'll get justice all the same! I have already given a bit of thought to how to find a way out. I'll tell you, write a letter to the Party Central Committee or the Central Control Commission. They'll phone us from there and inquire. That's for sure. We will put in a word for you. There is no time to lose. I heard they are turning you out. We must find a short cut."

I could not sleep that night, writing one version of the letter after another. Morning came and I took the envelope to the Kremlin. At the Troitskaya Tower control post I handed in the envelope addressed to Y. E. Rudzutak, Central Control Commission, C.P.S.U. (B.).

All the days that followed I was on tenterhooks. Some said nothing would come of it, others maintained that the Control Commission had so much to do that we would wait months before we would be summoned, and by that time we should have been thrown out of the plant for good. But two days later I got a telephone call and was told that Rudzutak would receive me within the next few days. A day later there was another telephone call and I was told that Comrade Rudzutak was expecting me at four that afternoon.

YAN ERNESTOVICH RUDZUTAK

Excited beyond all measure I headed for the Kremlin. My mind was concentrated on one thought only: to get to Comrade Rudzutak as quickly as possible and to seek his help. At last I arrived at his waiting-room. The secretary went in to announce my arrival and then invited me inside.

I walked in and on meeting one of the leaders of the Party and the Government I was overcome with timidness. Yan Ernestovich Rudzutak was at the time the Chairman of the Central Control Commission and the People's Commissar of the Workers' and Peasants' Inspection. A man of medium stature in a chamois leather sports jacket and a light shirt with a dark tie and wearing a pince-nez came out from behind the desk to meet me. We shook hands and he invited me to take a seat.

"Don't be nervous," he said noticing my agitation. "Calm down and tell me all about your troubles."

Rudzutak took off his pince-nez, wiped the glasses with his handkerchief and looked at me with encouragement.

I told him briefly of my work in aviation, stated my plans and complained of very difficult conditions for work.

"There are not so many aircraft designing bureaus in the country. Practically there are only two: Polikarpov's and Tupolev's," I said, "and to deal with our small group of young enthusiasts in such a way is a cruel and foolish thing to do! New designing bureaus should be created in the interest of the state. But the bureaucrats at the Main Aircraft Industry Administration and the director of our plant fail to see it. That's what has brought me to the Party for help."

While he was listening to me Rudzutak took off his pince-nez, put it on again, paced the floor, sat down and jotted something down on the pad. Then he questioned me about my work, asked what kind of airplane we had made, why it had had an accident and whether there was a chance of repairing it.

I did not try to conceal that in fact I had made a mistake which led to the unlucky accident and explained that the mistake had been due to the high speed of our airplane which had left behind the fastest fighters. We had made a step forward in attaining higher speed and for that had been thrown out of the plant.

"What are you working on now?" asked Rudzutak.

"Just recently we have completed a passenger airplane—an airmobile."

"An airmobile? That's interesting. Will it fly?"

"Certainly it will. That's what it's been built for. Besides, our airmobile can land in practically any clearing however small."

Comrades Kliment Voroshilov and Georgy Orjonikidze, members of the Political Bureau of the Central Committee of the Communist Party, visiting the Central Airfield

Yak-1 fighter

"You are not exaggerating things, young man, are you?" Rudzutak laughed. "I live near Gorki at Nikolina Hill. Near Maxim Gorky's country house. Could you fly over there?"

"I shall have to see whether the ground is suitable for landing there," I answered somewhat taken aback by the unexpected suggestion.

"I would like to see what your plane is capable of," Rudzutak said.

"Come to the airfield," I asked him, "and we shall show you everything."

"No! That's not so difficult to do at the airfield. It would be a good thing if you managed to fly over to our place."

"All right, we will try."

Rudzutak pressed a button and said to the secretary who had appeared in the doorway: "Arrange for Comrade Yakovlev to drive to Gorki and see whether his plane can land there near my country house. And about your letter—I shall consult the comrades at the Central Committee. I think they will probably take your side and soon you will be able to continue your work," said Rudzutak. "And if you fly over to the country house we will continue our talk there."

Rudzutak bade me a warm good-bye, and I left on wings of hope. The next day a car called for me and I drove off to Gorki with Piontkovsky.

WE CONTINUED OUR CONVERSATION

In front of the Rudzutak's country house which stood on the steep bank of the Moskva River there was a small water-meadow. We measured the meadow, criss-crossed it in every direction to make sure there were no ditches, ruts or hummocks and finally decided that it was quite suitable for landing.

On Saturday a call came through from the Kremlin and we were told that if the ground in Gorki was suitable, Rudzutak would expect us at his place. Early Sunday morning found Piontkovsky, Demeshkevich, our mechanic, and me at the airfield bustling about our plane. By nine o'clock everything was ready and Demeshkevich and I went off by car to Gorki to meet the plane. At Gorki we inspected the meadow once more, spread out a wind-T, built a fire at the edge of it and waited.

At exactly 11:30 a.m. Piontkovsky took off from the Frunze Central Airfield. At about twelve the red monoplane approached flying low and dipping its wings. It made a circle over the country house, approached against the wind and made a perfect landing.

Naturally, after a few minutes, people from the surrounding villages began to gather round the airplane. Comrade Rudzutak arrived almost at once. He congratulated Piontkovsky on his successful flight and made no attempt to conceal his surprise that we had kept our promise.

"I thought you would back out of it," said Rudzutak, "and treated our agreement as a joke. It seems that you mean business."

Rudzutak listened attentively to my explanations concerning the aircraft and then practically stunned me with a phrase: "Well, I must go up in your machine and see for myself what kind of airmobile it is."

I laughed his remark off as a joke. But in the meantime Piontkovsky started the engine and held the cabin door open: "Please get in."

I was worried and wondered what to do. Should I risk taking a People's Commissar, a member of the Political Bureau of the Central Committee, up in the air in a new aircraft under field conditions?

"What about you? Don't be afraid," Rudzutak laughed.

There was nothing to be done and I climbed into the cabin after him. Rudzutak glanced round the cabin, sat down and said: "It's nice here. A real motor car. Well, off we go!"

Piontkovsky taxied to the edge of the meadow and turned the aircraft into the wind. Demeshkevich and his helpers, with some difficulty, cleared the runway of people.

The pilot opened the throttle and we were off. Beneath us lay the Nikolina Hill, Zvenigorod and the Moskva River, meandering across the meadows and through the woods. After circling over Perkhushkovo once or twice, we headed towards Gorki.

"Nice work, I never expected it to be that good. It's a real airmobile," said Rudzutak joyfully.

Getting out of the cabin he thanked us for the ride, praised the machine once more and invited us all for dinner.

We went towards the country house in high spirits. Hardly had we time to sit down at the table, when we heard the clatter of horses' hoofs and loud voices outside, in the porch. Through the window I saw two riders. A moment later Rudzutak went out to meet the guests, but reappeared, took Piontkovsky and me by the arm and led us out on to the porch.

"Here they are, the law-breakers. Take them away," laughed Rudzutak.

I recognized Kliment Voroshilov as one of the riders and Anastas Mikoyan as the other. They shook hands with us and laughed.

"I saw some law-breakers land in a place which was quite unsuitable for landing," Voroshilov said gaily. "We could see the red plane from a distance. What's going on there? we thought, and came galloping here to investigate. And what do we see: air sportsmen. It seems Rudzutak has been baptized in the air. Splendid! What bold people airmen are!"

Kliment Voroshilov and Anastas Mikoyan soon left, wishing us success in our work. We stayed at the Rudzutak's the rest of the day. In the evening as dusk was falling Piontkovsky took off and headed towards the Central Airfield.

Back home I was in a fret. What was going to happen?

Events were not long in coming.

AIRCRAFT OR BEDS!

Soon after that incident I was summoned by Korolyov, the chief of the Aircraft Industry Central Administration. Before I was invited into his office, I had to wait for a long time in the reception room.

An amazingly fat, dark-haired man was sitting behind a huge desk. Casting an unfriendly eye over me he got down to business without greeting me and even without offering a chair: "Chucking you out of the plant, are they? Just the right thing to do. So now. I gave orders to accommodate your designing bureau and your technicians and workers at a bed factory on the Leningradsky Prospekt. Is that clear? Don't count on more. You may go. And don't go running about with your complaints, or—Well, go."

From now on we were firmly established. The manufacture of beds was soon turned over to some other factory, and we became the sole owners of the workshops. The makers of beds were trained to be skilled makers of aircraft. Soon after that I was appointed director of the workshops.

PERIOD OF RECONSTRUCTION

Life became easier for us when we obtained a real lathe. One day quite by chance I got acquainted with the chief of construction of the Moscow underground and told him of our difficulties. His administration was willing to help us and presented our workshops with a new and excellent DIP lathe.

We got the lathe, but could not bring it inside through the doorway of our machine shop, so we had to haul it in through the window.

After we got the lathe we began to call our workshops a plant. The lathe itself enjoyed special respect and honour for a long time to come; ultimately, after many years of service we turned the veteran over to a vocational school as a souvenir.

Korolyov, the chief of the Central Administration who felt no sympathy for us, left our firm in care of his deputy, Alexander Belenkovich, a lively and active man who understood what we were about and helped us to put our shops into shape.

With Belenkovich's help we started to replan the

workshops' layout and to add new shops. These completed the ensemble of the plant as it is now.

In spite of many difficulties we managed to build another new aircraft. This was the UT-2, a two-seat trainer, intended for training pilots at flying schools and aeroclubs. It passed the state acceptance trials and was put into production. The UT-2 was a monoplane and fast enough for aerobatics.

In 1935 the aircraft took part in an all-Union flight for sporting planes. Nearly thirty machines of various makes flew the circuit Moscow-Gorky-Kazan-Sverdlovsk-Orenburg-Kuibyshev-Saratov-Stalingrad-Stalino-Dnepropetrovsk-Kiev-Moscow—about five thousand kilometres in all.

The pilot was Piontkovsky; he and his flight engineer Demeshkevich brought our UT-2 in first.

I WANT TO BECOME A COMMUNIST

In the autumn of 1932 Piontkovsky and I handed in our applications for Party membership at the same time. We were to be accepted into the ranks of the Party at the same Party meeting.

The meeting took place in a large hangar which had been adapted for us as our club. The hangar was filled to capacity, and although the workers, mechanics and engineers, all those whom I met every day in the plant shops, at the airfield and at the designing bureau, were very well known to me a feeling of nervousness did not leave me for a moment.

One by one the workers and engineers who had handed in their applications went on to the platform.

Suddenly there was a stir and all heads turned towards the entrance.

There was a ripple of applause. I saw the tall, stoop-shouldered figure of a man clad in a light-grey coat with an embroidered skull-cap on his head. He was taken up to the front and offered a vacant seat next to me. I was so much preoccupied with my forthcoming appearance on the platform that I did not at first grasp who it was sitting next to me. And it was only when he smiled at me from under his thick moustache and stretched out his hand, as if I were an old friend of his, that I recognized Maxim Gorky. You can imagine how surprised I was.

This was at the period when Gorky, just back from Sorrento, was eagerly engaged in absorbing Soviet life, visiting factories and construction sites, meeting workers, scientists, Young Pioneers and pilots. Gorky made his appearance in workshops, at meetings, sizing up the people there, interested in everything, eager to know and see everything with his own eyes. Quite unexpectedly for everyone, he had appeared at the Party meeting of our aircraft plant.

The Yak-12 standard-bearers at the Tushino fly-past

A helicopter designed at the Central Institute of Aerohydrodynamics (1932)

I noticed that Gorky was breathing heavily and smoking a great deal. Scarcely having finished one cigarette he would light up another. Glancing around the hall he turned to me:

"I heard you are also joining the Party today?"

I nodded. How did he know that?

"Feeling nervous?"

I wanted to say "no" but I could not lie to Gorky, and said:

"Very, Alexei Maximovich."

At that moment Piontkovsky on the platform was telling the story of his life: a metal-worker, on the ground staff of one of the squadrons in 1917 he was obsessed by the idea of becoming a pilot. He learned to fly all by himself, then entered a flying school, went to the front, became flight instructor at a flying school; finally—a test pilot.

"Any questions?" asked the chairman.

"We know him!" came the shouts and applause from the gathering.

"Who is he?" asked Gorky looking at Piontkovsky.

"My friend Piontkovsky, a test pilot."

"Look, they are giving him a big hand. You don't have to worry," Gorky said and along with the rest he applauded the results of the vote: the

Party members accepted Piontkovsky into the ranks of the Party.

I don't know whether Gorky was interested in my autobiography as I told it to that meeting or whether he was keen that people with experience should write books but in any case he later suggested that I should write about myself, and give the story of a Soviet engineer in the making for the anthology *The Year of 1917*. I started writing the book time and again, and only now managed to finish it.

MEMBERS OF THE GOVERNMENT VISIT THE AIRFIELD

In the summer of 1935 J. V. Stalin, N. S. Khrushchov, K. Y. Voroshilov, A. A. Andreyev and A. V. Kosarev watched the performance of sporting aircraft at the Tushino Airfield. They mixed with pilots, parachutists and designers and watched the flights directly from the airfield, and not from a special stand, as had usually been the case during the Aviation Day fly-past.

The organizers of the display decided to show our new sports and training aircraft competing in flight with the old types. The pilots went all out in their attempts to outstrip each other. The ancient U-2 was the first to lag behind. Then other planes dropped behind one by one. The UT-2 surged ahead and streaked over the airfield first.

Stalin asked who the designer of the aircraft was. I was introduced to the members of the Central Committee and the Government. After landing the airplane taxied over to our group. Piontkovsky and I took turns describing our aircraft and its performance. Stalin enquired about the engine's performance and what could be done to improve on the speed of the airplane. He remarked that the trainers should not be too complicated for young pilots to master and that they should be so designed, that these young pilots could easily go over to combat aircraft.

The Government approved of our work. Some time passed and we designed a new trainer, the UT-1. We worked hard trying to build an aircraft for training fighter-pilots.

A little later K. Y. Voroshilov and G. K. Orjonikidze visited the Central Airfield. I told them about our work and our plans in detail, while Piontkovsky created quite an impression by taking the UT-1 up into the air and smartly running it through its paces.

The UT-1 and the UT-2, which had been built earlier, were put into mass production and thousands of these machines served at flying schools and aeroclubs.

A REAL PLANT, AT LAST!

The attitude towards us sharply changed after the work of our group had finally been appreciated. The decision was taken to turn the former workshops into a real aircraft plant. Funds were allotted for the construction of a designing bureau and production shops. In the meantime we had rebuilt our workshops to meet our requirements.

But our future now became bound up with the construction of the new building. The premises were cleared of about a dozen of tumbledown wooden buildings and of a tremendous amount of rubbish. A large building with shops, designing bureaus and services appeared in their place.

From the outside our plant did not look like an industrial establishment with its austere architecture, light-grey façade and oak-panelled plate-glass entrance doors.

The estate was planted with lilac bushes, decorative trees, bushes, hops and the fence was entwined with wild grapes.

WHITE SHADES, WHITE CURTAINS, WHITE SMOCKS

Desks for designers and draftsmen were arranged in two rows in a huge hall, well-lit, with big windows on both sides. In the evening electric lamps in milky-white shades gave a light as brilliant as day. Comfortable chairs, desk lamps, snow-white curtains created an agreeable atmosphere for our work. The designers were in white smocks like doctors.

Since they had to sit at their desks hunched over drawings all day we introduced a rule—at lunch time everyone had to leave the hall and the windows were thrown open to ventilate it. After lunching in the canteen people went for a stroll in the yard, which in fact looked like a garden, to get a breath of fresh air. Even in winter everyone had to leave the hall for half an hour during the lunch break.

Smoking was originally prohibited by a decision of the general meeting which was then made law on Director's orders. Many gave up smoking altogether to our advantage and to the great joy of their wives.

ORDER IN YOUR WORKING PLACE

The superintendents and foremen of our shop did not have separate offices; their desks stood in the shops by the machines. They did not spend much time behind the desks. By keeping in close contact with workers and designers they knew exactly who was doing what at the moment, kept track of snags and helped to overcome them. This closeness to the actual work of production did a lot of good to those superintendents who were inclined towards a bureaucratic approach in their work.

In this way every worker knew that his chief was keeping track of his work and was always ready to help if necessary and to reprimand anybody who neglected his work. By this means we brought aimless wanderings about the shop and time-wasting gossip to an end.

In the designing bureau, the rules were the same. My deputy and senior designers sat with the rest of the designers in the hall: this was useful for work and discipline.

Every designer was obliged to supervise the part of work he was entrusted with in the shop. Our designers were not desk types, they knew production methods inside out. And the workers for their part knew the designers and saw their good and bad points.

Our staff consisted of carefully selected people because our work depended on them: on those who worked at the bench in the designing bureau and on those who directed them. When sizing a person up for a job our principle was never to take on people who were always changing their jobs. If a man was always skipping from one factory to another he must be either quarrelsome or a slacker who did not like his trade. Most of those who worked with us were good hands and were in love with their trade. And that is very important, especially when creating a new aircraft, because aircraft are born as a result of the most complex creative effort on the part of a large body of workers.

WHERE DO WE BEGIN?

Of the many types of airplanes created by various designers, only a few, the very best, go into mass production and see operational service in the Air Force.

On receiving an assignment for a new aircraft the first thing I do is to think over the basic features of the future airplane.

The assignment itself determines the aircraft's features—the size of its crew, the nature of its armament and its flight characteristics—speed, range and ceiling.

The task of the chief designer is to embody these requirements in the most suitable form through trial and error of the constructional features. He wants his aircraft to possess not only the necessary combat performance, good stability and response to controls; he wants to make it simple in design and convenient for mass production.

When thinking over the future machine, you try to visualize its shape, combination of materials, type and performance of the engine, equipment and armament, airfoil and tail-plane cross-section.

One of the main problems in aircraft designing is to determine the most advantageous dimensions of an airplane and its flying weight as a whole and of each separate part.

When I was beginning my career as a designer I made the drawings, outlines and general plan of the aircraft myself. Today I explain my considerations in detail to the designers who embody my ideas on paper and make an outline of the new aircraft. Highly skilled designers, they are good graphic artists. They usually sketch out several versions of a new design.

In a preliminary study of these designs I make corrections until my idea takes shape. The initial work which determines the features of the future aircraft is done by a small group of the most experienced designers.

DRAWINGS. A MODEL. MOCK-UPS

Finally the best version is chosen and the general drawings go to the designing bureau for elaboration. The whole staff joins in at this stage and the work is taken up by groups of designers who work on the chief components of the design: fuselage, wings, controls, engine, landing gear, armament, tail-plane, equipment, etc.

The Yak-9 assembly line

Mi-4 helicopter designed by Mil

Engineers work out aerodynamic calculations which determine the performance of the future aircraft: speed, ceiling, range, stability and other features.

A special group is entrusted with the very important task of calculating the plane's stresses and strength. An aircraft is a structure where the two main principles—those of ruggedness and load—are locked in perpetual struggle. The aircraft must be rugged and light and these two characteristics are for ever in conflict. The task is to calculate with the utmost precision the exact strength necessary for the type of aircraft without adding extra weight.

A full-size model of the future airplane is made together with full-size drawings, as well as scale models to be tested in wind-tunnels. With the help of this model we can find the most advantageous arrangement for the pilot's cockpit, flight and control instruments and check the correct form of the future airplane before it is built.

The model is built of pine struts and plywood, it looks just like a real plane and gives a complete picture of the future aircraft. The model has to be accepted by a special commission.

Thus a large body of men is engaged in the work of creating an airplane in the period when it exists only on paper. They are united by a common project and work under an over-all control.

Everyone must work accurately, efficiently, under strict discipline, for the original creative designing effort, after being split up into integral parts, to result in one single whole—an airplane.

The chief designer at this stage "conducts the orchestra," directs the work of each designer and sees to it that all the paths lead to one objective, carefully thought-out and planned beforehand.

A number of larger parts and components cannot be drawn full scale on paper. These are drawn on plywood frames called mock-ups. The mock-ups and blueprints go to the workshop and aircraft patterns and parts are made from them.

An aircraft is a very complex machine requiring the combined skill of workers of many professions: joiners, duraluminium workers, riveters, metalworkers, turners, milling-machine operators, welders and many other specialists.

BIRTH OF AN AIRCRAFT

The most important and interesting moment comes when all the parts begin to converge in the assembly shop. First the large parts of an aircraft are made: wings, fuselage, tail-plane. This is where the work of the designers and aircraft makers is tested.

Sometimes it happens that parts made in shops are out of true and cannot be joined together:

when this happens the culprits have to make alterations and blush for their bad work.

When the airplane is assembled it is examined and tested. First of all the airplane is weighed, its dead weight and the centre of gravity is then determined and the reliability of every control system, instrument and piece of equipment is checked.

It is then stressed for ruggedness. Or rather a model copy is tested. This, of course, will not be flown. Usually, two or three exactly similar prototypes are built simultaneously, one of these undergoes static tests, and another is tested in flight, providing the stressing tests on the first prototype have been satisfactory.

The drag of the oncoming airstream exerts a certain load on all parts of the aircraft during flight. The higher the speed, the greater the load. In the process of designing and building the aircraft it is necessary to check that all the aircraft's parts can withstand the varying loads they sustain in flight.

This can be determined by mathematical calculations but these are not always absolutely accurate while the aircraft's airworthiness must be absolutely beyond doubt. Therefore each new type of aircraft is put to the ruggedness test before its first flight to check and make sure that engineers have made their mathematical calculations correctly.

All parts are exposed to the same loads in the laboratory, that they will meet under flight conditions and even with a margin.

For example, we have to find out the strength of a wing. Using various methods, the engineers conducting the tests put the wing under the stresses it will encounter in the air. Special instruments watch the behaviour of the structure under load and register any warping of the wing at different points. The load is applied to the wing until it buckles under the weight. Thus we can ascertain the stress the wing is capable of withstanding.

The fuselage, landing gear, hand and foot controls, engine mountings, control surfaces—everything stressed in flight is subjected to a destruction test.

If the results of the first prototype tests are satisfactory and the calculations are proved to be correct, the second is prepared for flight tests.

FIGHTER-PLANE

Every time during the fly-pasts over the Red Square or at the Tushino Airfield when the red fighters designed by Polikarpov streaked across the sky to the general admiration of the spectators, my heart skipped a bit. I was possessed by the idea of building a high-speed combat machine. In 1938 the Government suggested to several designers, myself included, that they should compete in creating a new fighter. I got down to work with great enthusiasm.

Everyone at our plant put a lot of effort and energy into the creation of this new fighter. As the work was nearing completion our enthusiasm mounted, and if at the beginning you had had to talk some people into staying after hours and putting in a bit of overtime, towards the end men stayed on voluntarily, in the designing bureau and in the shops.

At last our aircraft was ready! There it stood, beautifully streamlined, its wings outspread, ready to take off.

A few hundred members of our staff were in a state of unusual excitement. Each saw in the airplane a bit of his own work, everyone was glad and at the same time anxious: would the airplane make a good showing, or would it fail us?

When preparation for the first flight began the excitement reached its peak. The last few nights before the test I practically could not sleep. Everything had been calculated and checked, nevertheless, I lived in fear that there might be a slip in our calculations and that something unexpected might happen.

I do not know how, but practically everyone at the plant had learned the day and hour of the test flight. I saw our workers and engineers on the roof of our plant and at the airfield. They were just as excited as I as they watched our offspring begin to move.

My close assistants and I stood near the hangar. I was shaking all over. The blades of the propeller merged into a silvery disc, and a cloud of dust rose behind the plane: the pilot banged on full throttle. The airplane began to move.

The narrow gap between the ground and the plane widened with every second. The airplane came nearer and nearer. It roared overhead, gaining altitude steeply.

A sigh of relief escaped everyone present. Meanwhile, the airplane completed its second circle over the airfield.

Up till now everything had gone smoothly. But this was not all: how would it land? The airplane began to lose height and make a landing approach. That was a very important moment in the life of a new aircraft. The pilot confidently glided the machine in, touched down in the middle of the airfield and after a short run taxied to the hangar.

This was an occasion for cheering. We rushed to the airplane, virtually dragged the pilot out of the cabin and started to toss him up into the air.

Before Piontkovsky had a chance to say anything, I saw by his beaming face and smiling eyes that everything was all right.

After the first test flights it became evident that the new combat machine left all other aircraft of this type far behind in performance. It was decided to put the fighter into mass production. I was summoned to the Kremlin on April 27, 1939.

I had been at the Kremlin more than once attending official conferences and meetings, but this time I received a personal invitation. I was overcome by an unusual excitement. On my way to the Kremlin I tried to guess possible questions and think of my answers.

I was met warmly and asked to describe my work and the new aircraft.

As the conversation drifted further and further into the realm of technology, I found myself in my element. I felt less nervous and very soon I was completely at ease and answered questions without fumbling for words, as had been the case at the beginning of the conversation.

After a number of questions concerning my future work had been settled, Voroshilov wrote something on a slip of paper and with a sly smile showed it to Stalin who ran his eyes over it and nodded assent. Then Voroshilov read out the text of an application to the Presidium of the Supreme Soviet of the U.S.S.R. to award me the Order of

Lenin, a ZIS motor car and a hundred thousand rubles bonus.

This was a surprise and in my embarrassment I forgot to voice my thanks. I managed to stammer out that it was not I alone who had done the job and that it would be unjust to reward only me. I was told to make out a list of workers who had taken part in the creation of the aircraft to be recommended for awards.

As I said good-bye everyone wished me further success in my work.

In the morning the list of workers who deserved awards was drawn up at the plant and the Government decorated all those who distinguished themselves in the creation of the new aircraft.

FLY-PAST OVER THE RED SQUARE

Meanwhile another award awaited us: an Air Force unit which had received the first batch of our planes was slated to take part in the May 1 fly-past over the Red Square. It was a great honour for me as a designer and for all the workers at the plant.

For more than ten years I had watched the parade on the Red Square but never had I been so excited and nervous as on that day. For among other planes there would be our new high-speed fighters.

Professor Nikolai Zhukovsky, the father of aviation science

It seemed to me that the march-past of the infantry, mechanized units, artillery and cavalry would never end. And although the time-table of the march-past was known to me and I knew that our planes would make their appearance at noon sharp, nevertheless from the very first minutes of the march-past I kept glancing in the direction from where the planes would come.

At last the ground forces went by and a huge combined band of more than one thousand players from Red Army units marched past the stands.

It was only when columns of thousands of demonstrators flooded the Red Square carrying banners, streamers and portraits that the airplanes made their appearance.

Squadron after squadron of bombers rumbled over the Red Square in perfect flying formation. There were too many of them to count. They were followed in no less perfect formation by much faster biplane fighters flying in groups of five at regular intervals like waves on the sea-shore.

Fast monoplane fighters roared over the Red Square and disappeared beyond the Zamoskvorechye.

The throb of the engines died out and once more you could hear the noisy rejoicing of the holiday demonstration.

The uninitiated thought that the fly-past was over, but—what was that?

In the empty sky, several specks appeared between the towers of the Historical Museum. They rapidly grew in size. I gazed at the approaching group of planes until my eyes hurt. When the aircraft appeared over the square, I heard the shouts: "New fighters!"

They zoomed over the Red Square, climbed steeply and, diminishing quickly, vanished in the sky before the very eyes of the amazed audience.

My feelings at that moment were hard to describe. I was the designer of these new fighters that had gone hurtling over the Red Square.

CHAPTER THREE

SHORTLY BEFORE THE WAR

In 1933 a squadron of Italian hydroplanes Savoya-Marchetti-55 under the command of General Balbo paid a visit to Odessa. A year later the Soviet Government sent three heavy four-engine TB-3 bombers designed by Tupolev to pay the return visit. In those days TB-3s were the latest and most powerful bombers in the world.

I was included in the Soviet delegation.

The Italians drew up an extensive programme of receptions, visits and tours of Italian sights, aircraft institutions, plants and schools for us. On the day after our arrival we started out in huge buses for the airfield at Montecélio, the site of the research institute of the Italian Air Force.

Though as regards its air power, Italy had never been in the front rank, in its preparations for war the fascist government of Mussolini encouraged extensive record and sports flights, and spared no money on the organization of model institutions and airfields. At the Air Force research institute at Montecélio we saw a hydro-tunnel under construction, a well-equipped aircraft-engine test station, horizontal and vertical wind-tunnels for investigating aircraft spins.

We examined a few planes undergoing various tests. The high-altitude, record-breaking aircraft made by Caproni attracted our special attention. In that aircraft Donatti had established the world altitude record of a nearly fourteen thousand metres. We met Donatti himself—a lively, shortish pilot already in his forties. Then we were shown a military aircraft of the latest design in flight, and the aerobatic performance of the well-known Italian pilot Mario Bernardi in a Caproni trainer.

Most of the planes which were shown to us at Montecélio, including the latest types, were not original in design. The Italian aircraft people devoted their efforts to improving already existing types.

AT FIAT PLANT

We were surprised to note the difference in the equipment at the research institute at Montecélio and at the Fiat plant, the largest industrial enterprise in Italy. At the institute they doted on modern machinery and technology while the plant astonished us by its technical backwardness.

The Fiat plants were at Turin. The Milan-Turin highway which we took was thickly lined on both sides by Fiat advertisements. The people of Turin worked for Fiat. The Fiat motor-car plant, the Fiat aircraft plant, the Fiat machine-building works were all large enterprises employing thousands of workers. The magic word "Fiat" concealed a small group of capitalists, who ruled these plants and seemed to hold sway over the town of Turin itself.

We visited the Fiat motor-car plant. It looked nothing like our Soviet motor-car plants with their huge one- or two-storey buildings spread out over a vast area. The Fiat plant is situated inside the town limits. Cramped on all sides by the town the plant is built in a confined space. We inspected the four-storey plant without getting out of the car.

To save production space cargo lifts and car ramps were built instead of staircases. There was a roadway in the middle of the shop on each floor fringed on both sides by white traffic lines. These roadways were used to bring in the materials and equipment. Moving slowly along the shop roadways and ramps we watched the process of car making, beginning with the procurement shop on the ground floor and finishing up on the third floor in the assembly and paint shop. Finally we found ourselves on the roof of the building which had been made into a test-track for the cars assembled on the floor below. Wishing to make an impression on us our hosts took us round the track at a great speed.

Besides the motor-car plant we were shown an aircraft-engine plant, a diesel plant and the Fiat aircraft plant where among other airplanes we saw several new machines which were of no interest and made no impression on us.

Neither in the laboratories, nor in the shops, nor at the Fiat plants did we see a single interesting specimen of any modern equipment capable of thrilling the heart of an engineer.

The Soviet aviation delegation inspects new Fiat planes in Italy in 1934

One of Yakovlev's sports machines (1937)

CAPRONI

The impression which the plant of the oldest Italian designer, Caproni, made on us was even worse. We visited his plant when we were on the way to the International Aviation Exhibition in Milan.

Caproni was an elderly, dark-skinned, temperamental Italian, very active and energetic, with quick, sparkling eyes. He took us round the shops chattering animatedly about his plant.

"I began my career as a designer in 1910 without a penny in my pocket, but with a lot of enthusiasm," he told us. "There was a shed on the spot where we are standing now, in which I built my first aircraft. In the course of twenty years the enterprise gradually expanded. New shops and hangars were added. I had to build several of them across the road and connect the old and the new shops by underground tunnels."

The plant was something chaotic, with a complete absence of any planning; that was the impression that began to form in our minds.

Caproni showed us a small primitive wind-tunnel in which he tested the models of his aircraft. One look at the tunnel was enough to make us realize why the aerodynamic qualities of the Caproni aircraft were so low. You could not possibly construct modern aircraft using this primitive installation.

The aircraft plants in Italy developed rapidly during the war with Abyssinia. The Caproni and Fiat plants teemed with activity. However, they continued to put out airplanes of the old type. "To fight Abyssinia you don't have to have modern planes. What's the use of squandering money?" Caproni asked cynically.

Our acquaintance with the Italian aircraft industry was completed at the Fiat and Caproni plants. There were no more large aircraft enterprises in Italy worth showing and so we were given a treat of visits to historical sites and that was nothing to be regretful about.

VIENNA, 1934

On our return to Moscow in our TB-3s we stopped over in Vienna. The airfield had been surrounded by police long before our heavy aircraft landed there. Hardly had we stepped down on Austrian soil when we were requested to show our papers. No one was allowed near our planes except for the members of the Soviet Embassy and a TASS representative. Meanwhile, when making our landing approach we had noticed crowds of people running along the streets leading to the airfield.

Later we learned that the airfield was situated in the Floridsdorf District, the workers' suburb of

Vienna, where shortly before our arrival the troops and police stamped out an anti-fascist uprising.

We arrived on a Sunday and the working people seeing the giant Soviet planes with red stars on their wings making a circle low over the city rushed to the airfield to meet us. But they were not allowed to come near the aircraft. The police tried to beat back the crowds of workers from the buses in vain. The workers broke through the police lines and swarmed around us. Those who were near us shook our hands and patted our backs. I saw tears in the eyes of many. The plucky ones shouted "Rot Front!" and raised their clenched fists in greeting paying no heed to the ravings of the police.

The buses made their way slowly along the streets with the workers accompanying us on both sides running, riding bicycles and waving red flags.

This unexpected meeting with its vivid expression of love for the Soviet Union made a deep impression on us.

We stayed only one day in Vienna but that was sufficient for us to understand what the fascist order which had just been established in Vienna looked like. Vienna, the bustling European city, gay Vienna, was a dismal and painful sight. It was as if a state of siege had been declared in the city. The government buildings and the houses of the fascist leaders were barb-wired and heavily guarded. Many buildings bore the signs of recent fighting. Filled-in shell-holes looked like fresh wounds. Some houses had been completely demolished by shell-fire. Most of the shops were closed and the streets were practically deserted.

If it had not been for the manifestation of warm sympathy on the part of the Austrian workers our recollection of Vienna would have been most unpleasant.

Our take-off the next day was fixed for five in the morning. I don't know how the people of the neighbouring district found out about the time of our take-off but the fence round the airfield bristled with people. Many women came wearing red blouses or kerchiefs. The attempts of the police to disperse the crowd of people completely failed. Our planes rolled across the field one after another. At that instant red kerchiefs and small flags appeared in the hands of most of the men and women lining the fence; they were sending their greeting to far-away, dear Moscow.

OFF TO FRANCE

In the summer of 1936 I was sent together with a group of Soviet engineers on a business trip to France to buy Caudron sports aircraft from the Renault Company.

I had dreamed of going to Paris since I was a kid. And there I was in a train speeding to Paris from Moscow via Negoreloye. We left Warsaw, Berlin and Liège behind us and finally arrived at the French frontier. In contrast to the cold-looking, strutting uniformed, be-swastika'd Hitler officials we had seen en route, with their clipped speech which sounded more like military commands, in France we were met by friendly glances and open smiles. French speech seemed particularly melodious to us.

I had read much about Paris and when we went sightseeing everything seemed so familiar and so near and dear to me.

However, if our general impression of France and its people and especially of Paris was full of deep sympathy for this wonderful country and warm feeling towards its people, our acquaintance with French aviation left us disappointed and even bewildered.

At the dawn of aviation France had boasted the largest number of aircraft companies. French designers included the names of Blériot, Farman, Caudron, Voisin and others. At one time France held first place in the world in the number of new aircraft designed. Nevertheless, in 1936, three years before the war with Germany, the French aircraft industry was in a poor state.

We visited the plants of the well-known French designers Blériot, Renault-Caudron, Potez and the Messiers plant.

THE FATE OF DESIGNER BLÉRIOT

Situated in the Paris suburbs the small Blériot plant stood on the banks of the Seine surrounded by abundant greenery. Its founder and chief designer was Louis Blériot, the national hero of France and a pioneer of aviation.

Blériot was the first man to cross the English Channel from France in a plane in 1909. It was an outstanding achievement for those times, and the achievement made a great sensation all over the world. You can imagine our interest in the Blériot plant.

However, the plant and the attitude of the French officials towards the designer made the most painful impression on us. Part of the plant was closed down and some of the shops were working at half capacity. The plant experienced great material difficulties and was dying a slow death.

The experimental shop where several new types of aircraft were in various stages of construction amazed us by the disorder that reigned there. The work was proceeding on a small series of one-seater fighters. The experimental shop was really nothing but a primitive workshop, where coppersmiths hammered away with wooden hammers, rivets were made by hand and a number of parts were made and fitted in the same way as at the beginning of the century. Engine cowls and wheel fairings not only for experimental craft but also for serial airplanes were hammered into shape by hand on wooden mandrels.

Blériot at that time was an old bedridden man. He was unable to supervise work at the plant. We were met by Erbemont who had been Blériot's close associate during the entire period of his glorious career in aviation. He spoke of his teacher with great feeling and warmth and we could sense bitterness and indignation in his words that Blériot's services to his country were forgotten, although many wonderful flights glorifying French aviation had been made in his aircraft even during the latter years.

FRENCH AVIATION ON THE EVE OF WAR

The Renault-Caudron plant, also in the suburbs of Paris, made a more favourable impression on us. There was more order in the shops but the same primitive methods were used in making parts and assembling aircraft. At the airfield the company demonstrated all types of Caudron airplanes to us. Despite extensive and well-organized publicity and a number of really outstanding achievements (I have in mind the world speed records set up in low-powered Caudron airplanes in 1934-35), only two or three specimens of each type were ever built. Even the latest types did not find their way into the French Air Force.

Other enterprises which we visited also made a poor showing.

For a long time an opinion prevailed in France that more types of airplanes should be created so that the best could be picked out from among them. This played into the hands of the adventurers and swindlers of all kinds. They would hire a designer, produce a swarm of new types of aircraft, raking in money from the state and virtually swamping the French market with new types. The work of designers became hopeless and when war with Hitler Germany broke out the French army found itself without aircraft, or at least without aircraft that could stand up to the German planes.

LONDON AIR-SHOW

In 1936 I spent a few days in Britain with a group of Soviet engineers and designers.

The Royal Air Show was held annually in Britain. The show staged at the Hendon Airport near London was well organized.

We were given coloured cardboard passes with the numbers of our sector and place. We were to carry the passes on our coats attached to a button on a string. This relieved us of the tedious business of presenting it.

MiG-15 jet fighter

The two-engined Yak-4 combat machine

The show opened with air races of various types of planes. The planes took off simultaneously from the airfield, circled over it and landed. The race began and ended within the field of vision of the spectators.

Among others we were shown early aircraft, dating from the beginning of our century: the biplane made by the Wright brothers, the Blériot monoplane and other flying machines. These planes reminded me of the one I saw when a child at the Khodynka Field. They too looked more like kites or bookshelves than airplanes.

Their primitiveness was felt all the more strongly when fighters and bombers of various designs and latest models, appeared in the sky soon after.

A rather interesting aerobatic stunt was shown by a group of five fighters tied together by flagged ribbons before the take-off. Their movements were in perfect unison. Having taken off from the airfield they performed all their aerobatic manoeuvres and landed without snapping a single ribbon.

A PECULIAR STUNT

A fighter pounced on a flying bomber its machine-guns rattling away. The bomber was set on fire. We saw tongues of flame and a black trail of smoke. The effect was made with Bengal lights. The bomber crushed to the ground wrapped in flames. The spectators saw the bomber disappear behind a hangar and a column of smoke and fire billowing up into the sky. In reality the bomber disappeared behind the hangar and made off flying just above the ground while a smoke-screen imitated the crash.

Then followed a peculiar stunt.

A big crowd of armed, dark-skinned people apparently personifying Arabs burst on to the airfield from some concealed hiding-place. In white burnouses and head-dresses they rushed at the stands shouting and howling frightfully. The spectators were taken aback by the suddenness of their attack. But just at that moment fighters shot out over the roof of the hangar. Flying low above the airfield they "strafed" the "tribe" with their machine-guns and showered them with small bombs. Machine-guns rattled, "bombs" burst on the airfield before the very stands. The "tribe" was wiped out to a single man. We were the witnesses of a brief but very illustrative demonstration of methods of "humane" treatment of backward peoples.

ON THE NEXT DAY

The next day at its own airfield the De Havilland Company organized a display of the latest types and designs of British aircraft, engines, aircraft equipment and armament for the official representatives of the aircraft industries of many countries.

We were shown fighters, bombers and passenger planes. Aircraft engineers and designers of many countries climbed inside the aircraft, examined them and questioned pilots and mechanics keenly. I being a designer of sporting airplanes was attracted by the streamlined light planes. I examined the Miles training and sporting aircraft, a light biplane by the De Havilland Company and the twin-engine Monospar plane which at that time ranked as a technical novelty.

From light planes I went over to passenger aircraft and finally to fighters. Among the fighters I saw two new monoplanes: the Hurricane built by the Hawker Company and the Supermarine, the latest product of the British aircraft industry.

These were the same Hurricanes and Supermarine-Spitfires which a few years later became the backbone of the British fighter force defending England in 1939 against Goering's air pirates.

The Spitfire on display was the prototype, the first experimental aircraft of a type which was later turned out in thousands. Visitors were restricted from a close examination of the Spitfire for it was the latest British military secret. The machine was roped in and no explanations were given.

Years later, during the war I learned by chance from the *British Ally* newspaper published in Moscow that the designer of the Spitfire was Reginald Mitchell.

REGINALD MITCHELL

Mitchell took to aviation and plane-modelling while very young. At twenty this talented man became the chief designer of an aircraft plant. During the first year in his post he designed a seaplane for the International Schneider Trophy Races.

Schneider was a rich Frenchman, an aviation enthusiast, who established an annual prize for the aircraft clocking the best time in race. Britain, the U.S.A., France and Italy participated in the races. The rules of the races specified that the country which won the races three years running would retain the trophy for ever.

For the 1925 races Mitchell built a plane which caused quite a sensation. For the first time in aviation history people saw a fully streamlined machine. But just before the start of the races the plane suffered damage and could not take part in the races. The incident had grave consequences. The private company Mitchell was working for declined to finance the construction of his new airplane for the next year's race. For two years Britain took no part in the competitions. It was only in 1927 that the Royal Air Force decided to enter the races and allotted funds for the construction of the airplane. Mitchell built a streamlined, high-speed machine.

The races stirred up fervent passions. Mussolini with his usual boastfulness wired Britain in advance that the trophy would be won by Italy. But it was Mitchell's airplane that came first clocking 450 k.p.h. The Italian craft Makki-Castoldi did 434 k.p.h.

The next year the races were also won by the British. And once more the all-metal plane designed by Mitchell won.

Preparations for his third year in the competition were the hardest of all for Mitchell. Britain was experiencing an economic crisis and Parliament refused to provide money for the construction of the new machine. This time Mitchell's work was financed by a rich lady.

There was not enough time to build a new plane before the races and Mitchell decided to modify his last year's machine.

For the third time running his craft captured the prize in a 575 k.p.h. race. The Italians this time did not even dare to enter the race. The Schneider Trophy stayed in Britain for ever.

A MAN TO RESPECT

A very modest person, Mitchell put forward all his efforts to win the international races without a thought of glorifying himself. He realized that due to participation in the races valuable research material was accumulated in the field of high speeds which would come in handy for Britain one day.

In 1934 Mitchell began work on his Spitfire fighter. And about two years later his aircraft was on show among other planes on the green airfield at Hatfield. To our regret we did not meet Reginald Mitchell himself. He was severely ill and bedridden.

Realizing that he had little time to live Mitchell was in a hurry to finish his fighter. He died in 1937, the year his plane was put into mass production.

Two years after his death the Spitfire fought successfully against Nazi bombers raiding British towns. In the battle for Britain the Nazi Air Force suffered heavy losses from these combat planes piloted by courageous and skilful men.

IN HITLER GERMANY

Shortly before the fascists attacked the Soviet Union I happened to visit Germany with the Soviet economic delegation.

The Hitlerites at that time were engaged in a fierce air battle with Britain.

Germany was blacked-out. After crossing the border of our peaceful country blazing with the lights of hundreds of villages and towns we plunged into a realm of darkness and anxiety. The train sped past dark unlit stations towards Berlin with heavily curtained windows.

In Berlin life came to a standstill from nine o'clock in the evening until morning in expectation of British raids. Theatres and restaurants closed down, streets became deserted and people hurried down into the cellars to the accompaniment of the wailing sirens.

In the day-time all traces of the night's destruction were quickly and thoroughly eliminated. Children ran about along the sand and gravel paths in the parks among the green lawns and flower-beds. German *frauen* went to the market with their shopping-bags. People queued up at the food shops. Most of the men were in uniform of some sort: army, SS, police or a brown coat with a swastika arm-band.

In the rooms reserved for us at the hotel we found Berlin guide-books and all sorts of advertisements. A copy of *People's Art*, a German illustrated magazine printed on heavy glossy paper was lying on the table. On the front cover there was a soldier with a hand grenade in one hand and a pistol in the other posed against a background of the smouldering ruins of a city, and the caption: "Warsaw is ours!"

I leafed through the pages. Side by side with engravings, reproductions of well-known masters I saw the art of modern Germany lauding the war.

One picture has remained etched on my memory to this day: a dying German soldier, kneeling under a spreading tree, resting his head in the hands of an angelic-looking, pious maiden. The caption under the picture read: "The supreme calling of each German is to die for his Führer."

On the opposite page was the colourful picture of a heavy German gun with its crew bustling around it, while smoke billowed up from some structures on the horizon.

Such was the "psychological treatment" given to every rank-and-file German. It went on day after day, hour after hour, instilling in them the spirit of destruction, hatred of man and brutality—all the paraphernalia of fascism with which the Soviet people made their close acquaintance during the war.

At first the willingness with which the Nazi showed us their aircraft industry, one of the most secret branches of their armed forces, surprised me. But later on the clue was supplied by the Germans themselves.

Yak-17 jet plane

Heavy airborne troops glider Yak-14

One day we were invited to visit an aircraft plant in Oranienburg in the vicinity of Berlin. The plant was in perfect order. True, not once did we go to a plant without having to apply for the visit a week in advance stating our wish to inspect such and such plant. Thus we would come when everything was prepared for us. After our visit came to an end the head of the plant suggested that I write down my impressions and opinions of the plant in the guest-of-honour book.

I turned the pages back to see who had made contributions before. It turned out that we were not the first foreigners to be shown around the plant. Many well-known aircraft people from the U.S.A., England, France, Japan and other countries had visited the plant and made their entries.

The director of the plant pointed out to me the entry made by the commander-in-chief of the French Air Force, Viemann, who had visited the plant shortly before the war with Germany. The general highly praised the plant: "A magnificent plant which does honour and glory not only to the builders of the plant but to the whole German aviation."

The director looked at me slyly while I was reading the entry.

"Well, your plant deserves the appraisal," I said when I finished reading.

"The thing is," the director said, "that the French general was shown this modern German aircraft plant to make him realize and remember that German air power was far greater than that of France."

They tried to frighten the French, the British, they tried to frighten the Americans and hoped to frighten us.

I sensed the desire to plant in us the seeds of fear of the Nazi war machine, to infect us with panic in the face of the might of Hitler Germany, the panic which helped them to defeat others and which would help them to crush our own will to resist.

But they underestimated Soviet people!

WILLI MESSERSCHMITT'S BREACH OF ETIQUETTE

In Germany I dealt chiefly with the leaders of the German aviation industry. Willi Messerschmitt, the designer, was the most characteristic figure among them. He was tall, lean, with a big head, sharp, angry but clever eyes and a large-featured face. His raven-black hair had begun to thin noticeably. A morose man of few words and sullen looks, he put on a show of cordiality towards us,

Russians, with difficulty. We were told that Messerschmitt was a convinced Nazi.

We visited the important plants in Augsburg, inspected the twin-engine Messerschmitt-110 and the pride of the German fighter forces, the "invincible" fighter, Messerschmitt-109.

After all the questions concerning these planes had been exhausted, the conversation turned to the new fighter-plane, Messerschmitt-209 which the Germans veiled in secrecy, speaking practically in whispers about its high performance.

Naturally we wanted to see that plane.

When it was wheeled out on to the field, we saw that this was not at all what we were expecting to see. The plane before us was a first experimental attempt to convert the racing Messerschmitt aircraft into a fighter. This was evident to any aircraft specialist. Judging by what we saw, we could tell that the project was a failure and that the work on the aircraft had been suspended.

That day at our meeting with Messerschmitt we told him what we thought of the plane. He reddened, got agitated but in the end admitted that what we had seen was not the Me-209, and ordered the real Me-209 fighter to be shown us.

However our opinion was that this craft too was in a pretty raw state and would require much effort before it became a combat fighter. The machine had some organic shortcomings and it was altogether doubtful whether it could be completed at all. Subsequently our guesses were confirmed.

Stung to the quick by our critical remarks Messerschmitt got into a white heat, jumped up and said angrily: "You don't like it? That's your business. I think the machine is good!"

The Germans were unable to complete the Me-209 and it made no appearance against our planes during the war.

WORDS AND DEEDS OF OLD MAN HEINKEL

Heinkel, another German aircraft designer, was a completely different person from Messerschmitt. The latter was comparatively young and tall while Heinkel was an old, shortish, cock-eyed man.

Messerschmitt was morose, concentrated and reticent, while Heinkel enjoyed a good joke and was quick and lively despite his years.

Heinkel, like Messerschmitt, was not only an aircraft designer. He was a big capitalist who owned several aircraft plants in Germany. The Heinkel company produced the twin-engine Heinkel-111 bomber, the chief tactical bomber of the German Air Force.

The Heinkel-111 disgraced itself for the first time raiding defenceless Spanish towns, in 1937, when dictator Franco was engaged in stifling the Spanish Republic with the help of fascist Germany. In 1939 these bombers set fire to Polish towns and villages. Then they bombed the peaceful population of Belgium and France.

On June 22, 1941, Heinkel-111s were the planes first to drop their deadly load on our Soviet land.

Messerschmitt made no bones of his hostility towards the Russians and was very reluctant to show us his planes. Heinkel on the contrary pretended that he was telling us more than his government allowed him to do. In some cases he would even drop into a half-whisper as if sharing "secrets" with us.

Heinkel demonstrated his latest fighter-plane, the Heinkel-113 which we did not rate very highly. Though possessing good flying performance the plane was greatly hampered by its bad operational qualities.

The very first days of the war proved that the Heinkel-113 fighter-plane in which the Germans put great hopes was a complete failure because its operational procedure was too complicated for field conditions. It was one thing to make flights from the Heinkel airfield with its technical services, and quite another to operate from a front-line airstrip. Heinkel fighters disappeared from the Air Force soon after the beginning of the war.

Heinkel-111s were also taken off the production line in the course of the war. Heinkel failed to improve his machine so that it could compete with

Soviet bombers, and, what was most important, defend itself against Soviet fighters for whom when spotted it was a sitting duck.

JUNKERS AND FOCKE-WULF

The Heinkel firm had to yield the leading place to the Junkers Company.

The twin-engine Junkers-88 bomber which lasted with some difficulty all through the war showed more or less satisfactory combat and flying performance. True, in 1944, unlike the early years of the war, Ju-88 pilots began to get panicky during encounters with Soviet fighters. They only ventured on raids under heavy protection of Messerschmitt and Focke-Wulf fighters.

Focke-Wulf and Junkers are the oldest German aircraft-building companies. Their founders, Junkers and Professor Focke, had long ceased to have anything to do with their establishments. Junkers was in Hitler's bad books and died in disgrace shortly before the war. However, since the name of Junkers, the eminent scientist, had great authority in Germany, the fascists had left it as a screen. The German public learned that new Junkers motors and planes appeared but only a few knew that Junkers himself was long dead.

Focke was thrown out of his establishments and organized a small plant in the vicinity of Bremen which looked more like a shed or a stable. Nevertheless for many years to come his name symbolized the reliability of all Focke-Wulf products.

HERMAN GOERING'S CHIEF PILOT

The Focke-Wulf plants were headed by Kurt Tank, the former chief pilot of the Hitlerite minister of aviation Goering. When we arrived at an aircraft plant in Bremen Kurt Tank was presented to us as the plant's director, chief designer and chief test pilot.

Kurt Tank was a hefty man of middle height, with a well-knit body and rough features. His voice was hoarse, his eyes grey and harsh. He was a typical Prussian fascist. Both his cheeks bore the scars of student duels, a tradition with Prussian students to show their courage and adroitness. The scar was the visiting-card of the true Prussian Aryan.

During our first visit Kurt Tank climbed into the cabin of a trainer and demonstrated some aerobatic flying. There, that should leave you gaping, our chief engineer and director of the plant flies himself! After a whole series of aerobatics Kurt Tank landed, jumped down from the trainer and, smiling complacently, invited us to dine with him. He led the way to the workers' canteen and offered us seats at the common table.

"Don't be surprised, I always eat here."

We did not believe him, but it was an interesting experience for us to have our meal in the workers' canteen and not at a posh director's dining-room.

Rows of long tables seating ten people each lined the big canteen. Plates and spoons lay in heaps at the entrance. Each worker took his plate and spoon and went to his place.

The only exception made for us was that we were brought our plates and spoons.

Tank was indulgent: look at me, the democrat!

HOW GOOD IS TANK'S FIGHTER!

Kurt Tank was a great boaster. At a diplomatic reception he told us three Soviet engineers: "I have designed an outstanding fighter-plane capable of 700 k.p.h. (quite a speed in those days). Next time you visit me I'll show it to you. But don't tell it to anybody," he added mysteriously putting his finger to his lips.

Later when we were visiting his Focke-Wulf plant in Bremen I reminded him of his promise.

"It is very unfortunate," he said without batting an eye. "You see this plane had a crack-up only yesterday. I'm very sorry but I can't show it to you."

Yak-3 fighter

Workers inscribed on the propeller blades:
Over and above the plan for the front

At this, with a persistence matching his hypocrisy I said, "That's all right, we will see it as it is."

But he flatly declined to show us the plane.

As we had guessed he did have the airplane he was talking about. It was the Focke-Wulf-190 brought down so many times by Soviet fighters during the war. But its speed was not seven hundred kilometres as Kurt Tank had bragged but far below it. Perhaps that was the reason why he did not show it to us.

THE WAR

On January 9, 1940 I was appointed Deputy of the People's Commissar for Aviation Industry and the head of the department of experimental aircraft building and research.

The work was interesting but very difficult, because, for nearly eight years, I had to combine it with my designing work.

Usually I spent the first half of the day at the designing bureau and at the plant, and the second half, up till two or three in the morning, at my office at the Commissariat. It was the period when our aircraft industry was developing at a tremendous pace and we all worked with great enthusiasm. The re-equipment of our entire aviation with modern planes was in the offing.

And then came June 22, 1941, the war.

The whole world knew the true worth of the perfidious, mendacious, hypocritical Nazi clique which by that time had enslaved almost the whole of Western Europe. All the same, the attack staggered us.

During my recent visit in Germany I had come to know the Hitlerite war machine fairly well, especially its Air Force, and I was aware of the enemy's strength. Far from overestimating the might of Nazi aviation I did not share the belief of some Western specialists in its invincibility. But a sober evaluation of the situation made all of us realize that the Soviet Union would face hard trials. Long, stubborn and bloody battles lay ahead of us. Of all the armies of the capitalist world the fascist army was the most prepared for war.

HARD PRESSED

In the summer of 1941 the perfidious attack of fascist Germany placed the Soviet Union and its aircraft industry in a very difficult position. Prior to the war we tested and put into mass production the MiG-3 (designed by Mikoyan and Gurevich), the LaGG-3 (designed by Lavochkin, Gorbunov and Gudkov) and the Yak-1 (by Yakovlev) fighters, the armour-plated ground-attack stormoviks Il-2 and the Il-4 bombers (Ilyushin), the Pe-2 light bombers and the Pe-8 heavy bombers (designed by Petlyakov). But the plants were just starting production and were unable to meet the requirements of the vast front.

The production of these machines increased day by day.

In the course of the war some of the models were discarded, others on the contrary were adopted by the Air Force. Thus, for example, as early as November 1941 we stopped producing MiG-3s and in 1943 we dropped making Il-4 bombers. By the end of 1944 a new machine, the Tu-2 bomber (designed by Tupolev), made its appearance at the front.

Throughout the war Soviet fliers fought the fascist invaders in Yakovlev and Lavochkin fighters, in Ilyushin and Petlyakov stormoviks and bombers. Beginning with 1943 the aircraft industry turned out nearly forty thousand of these machines annually together with the low-powered U-2s and UT-2s.

At the beginning of the war we had an insufficient number of planes and the Soviet Air Forces suffered heavy losses—a fact which the Germans turned fully to their advantage.

Moscow and other towns with large aircraft and engine plants were heavily raided by enemy bombers.

The production of new types of airplanes was enormously complicated by the necessity of evacuating these plants east to quieter and less vulnerable areas.

Thousands of trainloads of aircraft-plant equipment were sent beyond the Volga to the Urals and Siberia. Tank, artillery, motor-car and small arms factories and plants were evacuated together with them.

How long it will take to set them up in new places? When would they begin production? The success of Soviet troops—infantry, fliers, tankmen, artillerymen bravely fighting the Hitlerites depended on this.

Our designing bureau and the plant turning out Yak fighter-planes in series were evacuated to Siberia. A recently built aircraft plant was operating there but it made few machines and its production facilities were used very ineffectively.

We loaded our equipment and staff into trains in September when enemy raids were at their heaviest.

Those were difficult and anxious times for Moscow. Air-raid warnings were given several times a day, AA guns thundered and bombs fell. But the loading did not stop even for a moment. Thousands of people and complicated and bulky machinery had to be transferred far beyond the Urals in the shortest possible time. Moreover, even while being dismantled the plant continued to produce aircraft. Each machine was moved off only after it had turned out all the parts required for the number of aircraft scheduled.

Many trainloads of equipment were already on their way to Siberia while the assembly shop was finishing planes which were turned over to front-line pilots right there in the yard of the plant. They were fuelled with petrol and very often the pilots would take their machines up into the air and fly off on a combat sortie straight away. Thus the planes often had their first tests in encounters with enemy fighters.

PLANTS ON WHEELS

Rolling up their sleeves, designers loaded the train side by side with workers and employees. The work went on round the clock. Special care was taken to make sure that the expensive and fragile equipment of the designing bureau and laboratories arrived at our place of destination safely. Each foreman, worker and engineer made sure everything needed for the speedy organization of production was taken to the new site.

The Aviation Industry Commissariat worked

under tremendous strain in those days. Practically all the main aircraft plants were on the move. Everything had to be organized to ensure their arrival at the new sites as quickly as possible and start them in production with a minimum loss of time.

I decided to ride down to Khimki and see for myself how the loading and expedition of trains was proceeding. The car sped along the Leningradsky Prospekt, past the Dynamo Stadium, across the bridge over the canal and finally turned off the highway and drove up to the railway siding belonging to the plant. Hundreds of people were bustling about near the train standing at the wooden platform to which a continuous string of trucks was bringing machines. I made my way towards the train through the noisy bustle. The train was already loaded and final preparations were being made before it pulled out.

COME TO OUR HOUSE-WARMING

Workers looked out of the box-cars, jumped down and gathered round me. Everyone was excited but I could not spot a single gloomy or sorrowful face.

"Come to our house-warming." It was an invitation to one of the box-cars. Double tier bunks with mattresses and rugs thrown over them, an iron-stove in the middle, a table and chairs and a paraffin lamp dangling from the ceiling. Inquisitive children's eyes peered at me from the bunks. Women were already busy with their cooking.

"We are comfortable enough. If only we get there before the frosts," said Mikhail Glazkov who was in charge of the loading.

"You'll get there before the frosts," I replied. "What about the food?"

"We've managed that, we've organized a special canteen car in every train and put our people to work there. We have enough food to last us for the journey, and we have arranged for hot water to be available throughout the day."

"And who's to maintain order en route?"

"Each train has its commandant, usually one of the shop superintendents. They'll manage."

There was a clanging of buffers and the cars lurched and jolted.

"There's our locomotive. We'll be off in a moment. Come on out, Alexander Sergeyevich, or we'll take you with us," laughed Glazkov.

I took leave of the inhabitants of the car and stepped out on to the platform. The locomotive already had steam up at the front of the train.

I saw Mikhailov, our shop superintendent and now train commandant, running towards me.

"We're off!"

"See you in Siberia!"

TO THE FAR-AWAY SIBERIA

Fresh trains of forty box- and flat-cars loaded with workers, machines and materials set out every eight or ten hours from this platform for Siberia.

Hard as we tried to make things for our people as comfortable as possible, we realized that it was still very difficult for the thousands of them who were burdened with small children to move to Siberia in cramped box-cars.

It took the trains weeks to complete their journey. Winter came and frosts set in. There were food difficulties. But everyone realized that the country was living through hard times, they realized the significance of events and knew that they must weather all the hardships and privations.

Great was the heroism of people who, exhausted by a long weary journey, arrived in far Siberia in winter and started to turn out airplanes in an incredibly short space of time.

While trains were still being loaded in Moscow, in Siberia preparations were made to receive workers and staffs and equipment. Shops were arranged, production plans were drawn up, electric power, compressed air, steam and water mains were laid on to put the machines into operation immediately on arrival.

Barracks were put up for the workers in which each family was given a room.

Yak-23 jet fighter

Yak-11, a two-seat fighter-trainer

On arrival, it took two or three days for people to establish their new homes, unload the trains and arrange the equipment in the shops. Six days later the plant began to operate.

I had had no idea myself that it would be possible to organize the evacuation so efficiently and with so little time lost for the production of aircraft.

It makes me proud to recall that only three weeks later, the production of planes started to pile up every day and even every hour. In three months we not only caught up with our Moscow output level but considerably outstripped it. Eleven months later we were turning out seven and a half times more aircraft than in the pre-war period.

If, before the war, we had been told that thousands of plants could be moved elsewhere in the country and put into operation in such a short time many of us would have laughed. But what yesterday seemed impossible today became the reality.

AIR-RAIDS

I remember Moscow in the autumn of 1941. It was grim, cold, austere, deserted: the women and children had been evacuated to the east. My family too was evacuated. All my private interests and peace-time habits were quickly forgotten. As a rule we worked at the Commissariat till two or three o'clock in the morning. More often than not I would stay for the night at the Commissariat where some offices were turned into bedrooms.

Visits to plants and airfields, work at the designing bureau, important conferences in governmental bodies, endless telephone calls—twenty-four hours were not nearly enough to attend to it all.

Enemy aircraft would appear over the city. During the entire war the Hitlerites never succeeded in breaking through to the city in large numbers and causing it heavy damage; nevertheless during the raids we would hear the boom of bomb explosions and see columns of smoke and fires, now in one end of Moscow now in another.

We had a rule at the Commissariat that we went down to the shelter during air-raids. A special communication centre was set up there so that the People's Commissar and his deputies could keep in constant touch with all our aircraft establishments.

Our aircraft plants got off lightly although the Germans had them marked on the maps found on the pilots in shot down planes.

Moscow presented an unusual sight during an air-raid. Speeding along the deserted streets in a car on a summons to some governmental body I hardly recognized the city. The searchlight beams at night, the thunder of anti-aircraft guns and the rattle of AA shell splinters on the asphalted pavement were the only evidence that Moscow was alive and fighting.

AT THE BOLSHOI THEATRE

The war welded people together. Life without our families, the continuous danger, the necessity of spending most of the time together and the need for mutual support in work and in our private lives made people stick close to one another.

Work went on better and there appeared a special warmth and comradeship in our relations. We began to get the feeling of our neighbour at our elbow in the same way as did the soldiers in the line. That gave us real moral support.

Once after an air-raid I returned from the bomb-shelter to my office tired and exhausted after many wakeful hours of intensive work at the office. Glancing through the newspaper I noticed that they were showing the ballet *Swan Lake* at the theatre affiliated to the Bolshoi. I was seized by a desire to have some rest, some distraction from my duties. In a few minutes I was ready and off I went to the theatre.

Like everything else in the city, the theatre had changed. The stalls, boxes and the balcony lacked the usual gay pre-war crowd, dressed in its Sunday best. Instead, the unheated theatre was mostly filled with soldiers and officers who had got one or two days' leave and come from the front lines for a spell of rest.

The distinguished conductor, Faier, appeared on his stand, the opening strains of music filled the hall, the curtain went up and I found myself in the fairy-tale world of the *Swan Lake*. Chaikovsky's enchanting music played by the wonderful Bolshoi orchestra, the bright decorations and costumes, the graceful, light-footed ballerinas fleeting across the stage touched my innermost being.

I did not have the chance to see the performance through: I was summoned to the Commissariat during the third act.

IT WAS HARD TO PART WITH MOSCOW

The most anxious days of all came soon after October 10. The Germans were closing in on the city.

In the morning of October 15 I was summoned by the People's Commissar Alexei Shakhurin who told me that the Government had instructed him to evacuate all the designers immediately and that I was responsible for their evacuation.

The Government thought it necessary to put designers beyond all reach of danger and to move them far into the rear.

We had already evacuated the staff of our designing bureaus with the plants in the trains. Now it was the turn of our head designers. When I got back to my office I decided to ring up Ilyushin, Polikarpov, Arkhangelsky and others immediately.

The task proved to be far more difficult than the solution of the most complicated technical problem. They all thought up some reason or other for saying that they were not ready to leave immediately.

I got Polikarpov on the line:

"Nikolai Nikolayevich, how are things with you? Have you finished evacuating your plant? Did you manage to ship off everything? And all the people left? Good, now you have to go too."

"Where?"

I told him the name of the town.

"But how?"

"Just as you like," I told him. "If you wish to fly, I'll put you in contact with the people at the airfield and they'll tell you when to be there. If you wish to go by train, I'll book a berth for you. You can go by car if you wish."

But it turned out that Polikarpov could not leave immediately: he had to take his sister who lived at a country house forty kilometres away from Moscow. For half an hour I tried to make Polikarpov realize the necessity of his immediate departure, that same day, by any means available.

At last we settled that Polikarpov would start from Moscow by car that night at eleven. At eleven I decided to check up on him to make sure he had left. He had not.

"Nikolai Nikolayevich, why didn't you leave?" I asked him.

"Don't you see the weather? It's a regular blizzard outside. I better wait till morning."

No one would believe that he really had to leave his beloved Moscow where he had lived all his life. Everyone was clutching at any excuse to stay in Moscow for even one hour more.

A HORRIBLE NIGHT

Despite all the difficulties I in one way or another managed to get everyone off by midnight.

It was getting on for one o'clock when I was called to the Commissar.

"Well, how are things going on with the designers?"

"They've all left."

And I went on to tell him who left where and how. The Commissar was sitting behind his desk, he looked tired and spent with his grey face and red-rimmed eyes heavy with lack of sleep.

The Kremlin telephone rang. Anastas Mikoyan was on the line enquiring whether all the designers had left. The Commissar gave Mikoyan a personal account of each.

Then I heard him saying:

"Yes, he is here. Been busy all day sending off the designers and now he is here with me."

After his talk with Mikoyan, the Commissar told me that I was ordered to leave too. I was not ready to go yet and, just like the rest of the designers whom I had to persuade earlier in the day, I began to try and wheedle a postponement of my departure.

"Can't it be put off until tomorrow? I'll leave by plane."

"You heard what Mikoyan said. Carry out your orders."

I had thousands of reasons which it seemed would prevent me from leaving immediately but I had to carry out the order.

The rest of the night was spent in preparations for the journey. It was a horrible night. I had to go down to the plant for some papers, look in at my home to pick up my things and lock up the flat. I had to say good-bye to my comrades who were staying behind at the plant, to give all the necessary instructions and finally to be back at the office.

At six in the morning of October 16 I drove out of Moscow in a Pontiac.

ACROSS THE PITS AND DITCHES

We reached Ryazan quickly and without any incidents. Here was where our troubles began. The asphalted highway came to an end and we had to make our way along a sodden, battered dirt-road.

After half an hour's drive from Ryazan our cream-coloured Pontiac was plastered all over with dripping mud. Time and again we had to get out, to give the car a push and wipe the windscreen. Very soon we became as dirty as the car.

My driver Misha Sushchinsky had been foresighted enough to bring along two pairs of high rubber boots for himself and me which came in very handy: I put mine on and wore them for the rest of the journey.

After two days of ploughing through wet, clinging mud we and our cars had practically reached the end of our tether.

In addition, we had to be very careful.

At night somewhere near Ryazhsk our column of cars stopped, headlights were switched off and we heard the rumble of planes in the sky. We spent a few minutes in complete silence and started on our way again only when the planes had vanished. Finally we came to a village which looked like the end of the journey for us. The three-tonner which we sent ahead of us got stuck in the

Andrei Tupolev

mud and was unable to help us any more. A reconnaissance we sent out on foot returned and reported that we could not proceed any further. There was only one thing for us to do: to make our way towards the railway line.

We set off across country. Then for a while we moved parallel to the railway embankment.

When we got to the level crossing we drove our cars on to the track and headed towards Michurinsk, bumping over the sleepers. Luckily there were no trains and we were only five or six kilometres from the town.

In Michurinsk we learned that the road on was even worse and we had no choice but to continue our journey by train.

With the help of local people we quickly loaded our cars on to the flat-cars. And the rest of the way I made in the car riding on the flat-car, and, mind you, without a ticket.

TESTS CONTINUED AT THE FRONT

By the time the Germans attacked the Soviet Union, our first Yak-1 fighter-plane had successfully undergone its tests and had been put into mass production at one of our plants.

At the beginning of the war the plant turned Yak-1 fighters over to the military acceptance commission daily, although in small quantities. By this time the fighter had been through its official trials and had also been tested by Air Force units.

First of all each new experimental plane has to pass official trials during which its performance and basic flight characteristics are determined and the expediency of its adoption by the Air Force decided. However, only a prototype is subjected to official trials and although they give a general idea of the plane's performance these trials are nevertheless quite insufficient to show what the airplane is really capable of when operated under field conditions.

Therefore after the prototype has gone through its official trials successfully and has been adopted for operational service in the Air Force and put into mass production, an Air Force unit is set up in which three dozen of the new serial machines undergo full-scale trials under conditions closely resembling those at the front.

The airplanes operate from an airstrip which lacks the facilities of the aircraft plant's experimental airfields, and is without its smooth, concrete runways. There are no hangars and the planes are parked out in the open. No more hothouse conditions for them. Pilots take them up for mock dog-fights, low-flying attacks, high altitude and long-range flights. In these flights all the shortcomings usually come to light, are carefully studied and the designer sits down to ponder how to eliminate them efficiently and quickly. Strictly speaking the work of elimination of shortcomings of this or that aircraft continues all the time the airplane is in service, beginning with the official trials, then tests in an Air Force unit and finally in combat sorties in which thousands of airplanes take part.

The airplane goes through a lot of combat hours and all its faults are detected and eliminated. The plane becomes, so to speak, perfect—and then it has to be taken off the production line to make way for more up-to-date machines which too have to be cured of their "infantile diseases."

WE CURE AIRCRAFT'S "INFANTILE DISEASES"

Among the most common faults inherent in new aircraft are all sorts of leaks in the piping and connections. For instance, fuel is fed from the fuel tanks to the engine along very thin duraluminium pipes which are intricately interwoven with the air frame. When the engine is working, the pipelines and the fuel tanks vibrate very slightly. Due to this vibration cracks appear here and there and petrol starts leaking.

This is a very dangerous flaw and may cause a fire in the aircraft. To prevent this happening, the pipes are reinforced in the places where the vibration is most intensive or flexible tubing is substituted for the duraluminium pipes.

A powerful engine generates a tremendous amount of heat, part of this is due to the high friction of the moving parts, part to combustion. This heat, of the order of several thousand calories, is removed by the oil which is forced through all the parts of the engine subject to friction. The hot oil is then forced through the oil radiator where it is cooled in the airstream and returns to the engine so as to be heated once again and carry the heat away to the oil radiator.

The oil radiator, oil pump and piping are susceptible to vibration which causes cracks and oil leakages. And the loss of oil spells death for an aircraft because without it the engine and all the moving parts immediately break down.

Water pipelines and radiators made of delicate copper and aluminium pipes are also painfully susceptible to jolting and vibration. In a word, until the water, oil and fuel systems are tested and checked in the course of long service they are very susceptible to infantile diseases.

There are many more unpleasantnesses which lie in ambush for the designer at every step.

Our Yak-1 was no exception to the rule. We went through it all in 1940 and in the first months of 1941 and at the beginning of the war the Yaks

Academician Sergei Chaplygin, prominent Soviet scientist in the field of aerodynamics

were found fighting the enemy side by side with Ils, Las and other Soviet machines. But there were so few of them.

RAID OVER FOUR ENEMY-OCCUPIED COUNTRIES

As the war progressed Yak-1s were produced in greater numbers and that created another problem —training pilots. Students learned to fly in slow trainers but then they had to fight in fast fighter-planes. An intermediate aircraft between the trainer and Yak-1 was needed and very soon we came up with the Yak-7 trainer-fighter.

In the summer of 1943, after defeating the Germans near Orel and Kursk, our army approached the Dnieper, driving the fascists before them.

The designers of combat aircraft were summoned before our highest bodies and the situation at the front had been explained. We were told that the German Air Force was preventing our troops from crossing the Dnieper. Soviet infantry and tanks were pushing forward so fast that airfield crews were unable to keep up with the ground forces and prepare airstrips for the fighter units. The range of our fighters was insufficient to provide an air cover and keep off German bombers during the crossing. The Germans were taking advantage of this and preventing all our attempts to cross the river. We were ordered to extend the operational range of our fighters in the shortest time possible.

We went on working further in this direction throughout the war. In 1943 the Yak-9D (D stands for *dalny*—long-range—*Tr.*) made its appearance in Air Force units. It had a range three times that of a normal fighter. At the beginning of 1944 a group of Soviet fliers flew in Yak-9Ds non-stop from the U.S.S.R. to Italy, across occupied Rumania, Bulgaria and Yugoslavia.

This flight took place in broad daylight in full view of the enemy who only gaped at the fast-flying fighters. The flight was to Bari, a port in Italy, which had just been liberated by the Allies and was part of the mission carried out by order of the Soviet Government to help the People's Liberation Army of Yugoslavia.

HEAVY FIGHTER

The large calibre 37 mm. aircraft cannon was a wonderful creation by the aircraft armament designers and made its appearance in 1942. It was intended to be mounted in fighter-planes and the task of the day was to develop a heavy cannon fighter.

We put in a lot of intensive work and turned out the Yak-9T (T stands for heavy) in record time. It was the first heavy fighter armed with a cannon. It went through its official trials and then its trials in Air Force units practically without a hitch and was put into mass production.

It made life hot for the German bombers: direct hit by a 37 mm. shell reduced any fascist plane to a heap of flying rubble.

Later on, in order further to increase the fighter's firing power, we mounted a 45 mm. cannon and towards the end of the war replaced it by a cannon of a still larger calibre.

At the same time we worked to increase the speed of aircraft and succeeded in developing a fast light fighter, the Yak-3.

LIGHT FIGHTER

In the Yak-3 which appeared in the summer of 1943 we tried to include all the positive qualities and do away with all the shortcomings detected in the Yak-1, Yak-7 and Yak-9 aircraft.

But the main feature of this plane was its light weight. Our aim was to make the Yak-3 the lightest fighter-plane ever. But, of course, not at the expense of cutting down on its fuel, fire power or armour. On the contrary, having achieved the very small weight of only 2,650 kg. (300 kg. less than in Yak-1), we improved the aircraft's combat performance.

Its fire punch was increased by supplementing

its single 20 mm. cannon with two 12.7 mm. machine-guns instead of the 7.6 mm. ones installed in the Yak-1. By cutting down on its weight and improving the plane's aerodynamic form, that is, by streamlining it still further, we got a 70 k.p.h. gain in speed, while retaining the original Yak-1's 1,250 h.p. engine and increasing its ceiling and manoeuvrability.

In the autumn of 1943 the Yak-3 was adopted by the Air Force and was put into mass production. Already in the very first encounters with enemy planes it demonstrated its very high combat performance.

Soviet pilots spoke highly of the new fighter and this was the highest award for all of us who took part in the creation of the aircraft.

French pilots of the Normandie-Niemen Aircraft Regiment who had flown British Spitfires and American Aerocobras and Mustangs, when given the opportunity to choose any plane before going to the front, made the Yak-3 their choice.

WHAT PATH TO TAKE!

Before the war there was a clear-cut tendency in fighter aviation towards an increase in the gross weight of fighter-planes.

The war proved this tendency to be wrong. Already during the war Britain had to call off attempts to re-equip their forces with heavy machines such as Hurricanes and Tornadoes and concentrate upon Spitfires, the lightest of all the British fighters and the only ones which could successfully take on the light German Messerschmitts.

The American Thunderbolt did not prove its worth and invariably lost against lighter and more manoeuvrable enemy fighters. During their heavy bomber raids the Americans were compelled to use Thunderbolts as ground attack planes to silence German flak. Thunderbolts formed the first wave with the task of dealing with enemy AA installations. They were followed by formations of heavy bombers, with lighter Mustangs as escorts to ward off attacks by enemy fighters.

Even the Germans, who before the outbreak of the war had light fighters such as the Messerschmitt-109, were seized by the idea of developing a heavy fighter. During the war their backroom boys produced the Focke-Wulf-190 weighing nearly four tons. True, it had greater fire power and stronger armour than Messerschmitts but neither reinforced armour nor added fire power could prevent the latest German Focke from being licked by Soviet fighters.

The German designers realized their mistake too late: the Focke-Wulf was in mass production and to halt production of one type of aircraft and start producing another is a very complicated business, especially in war time.

The test of war proved that Soviet designers were right when they resolutely took the path of developing the light fighters which dominated the air throughout the second half of the war.

ENCOUNTERS WITH AIR PIRATES

Much could be said about the deeds of Soviet aviation during the war.

Soviet pilots and their formidable planes played a decisive role in defeating the fascist hordes at the Orel-Kursk Salient. At that time Hitler still believed in the "invincibility" of his troops and aviation, in the miraculous strength of the latest heavy Tiger and Panther tanks and the Ferdinand self-propelled gun. By the summer of 1943 the Germans concentrated a vast amount of infantry, tanks, artillery, bomber and fighter aviation near the towns of Orel and Kursk. The Nazi command had decided to seek revenge for Stalingrad. Their HQ had calculated the blow with mathematical precision but our command guessed the enemy plan and the time and place of their offensive.

A powerful group of Soviet troops armed with latest heavy tanks, anti-tank guns, fighters and stormoviks was concentrated in the vicinity of Kursk and Orel.

The decisive battle began.

The duel of thousands of artillery pieces on both sides merged into a continuous rumble, turning the earth into a sea of fire, smoke, flying lumps of earth and fragments of houses.

Guns, tanks, everything got mixed up. And the day became dark as night.

At that moment nearly six hundred German planes rose heavily into the air and converged like a dark cloud upon our forward lines carrying a lethal bomb-load.

Suddenly hundreds of forest clearings and openings, groves, the peaceful edges of woods and fields of stubble came to life. One thousand Soviet Yaks, Las, Ils and Pes roared from behind haycocks and out of the woods and took off raising clouds of dust with their propellers. The air reverberated with the roar of their engines. More than one million h.p., housed in engines designed by Klimov and Shvetsov, hurtled forward to meet the Nazi air pirates.

AIR BATTLE

An unprecedented air battle took place. When red-starred fighters clashed with German bombers and their escorting fighters, it was hard to tell from the ground who was who in that mass of planes in the air. Hundreds of dog-fights took place simultaneously before the eyes of our infantrymen, tanks and artillerymen.

Every minute you could see German planes falling out of the sky, some torn to pieces by shells from the heavy cannons of our fighters, others trailing fire and smoke behind them. Now and again you could hear the explosions of bombs as the enemy bombers which had been shot down blew up.

Dozens of parachutes belonging to German pilots who had managed to bail out hung in the air.

Very soon it was all over. The Nazi Air Armada was smashed to pieces: most of the German planes were destroyed, the rest turned tail. Our fighters went after them.

Soviet aviation had scored a complete victory.

BATTLE OF ENGINES

The victories of the Soviet Air Force were possible owing to the stamina and valour of pilots who proved their superiority over the Nazi "aces."

But the war which we had won was also a "battle of engines." Even the most courageous army can be defeated if it is not armed with first-rate weapons and equipment, and these can be more perfect and better than the enemy's only if the country's level of science and technology is high enough. Of exceptional importance is the role of a designer who is called upon to embody the latest achievements of scientific and engineering thought in his creations.

A designer is a creator of new technique. Advance in arm's production depends on whether the designers in this or that branch are progressive in their ideas and whether they are capable people.

Aviation is one of the decisive arms. In the 30s, when there was the first whiff of war in the air, especially beginning with the events in Spain where Hitlerites sided with the fascist Franco and helped him with military equipment against the Spanish republicans, feverish competition between the designers of all the countries ensued.

Since the designers worked in secrecy, each country went its own way. Designers all over the world and especially German, Soviet, British, U.S., Italian and French designers, were engaged in under-cover competition. Tense and silent, this competition raged in research centres, designing bureaus, laboratories and experimental plants.

When the Hitlerites attacked the Soviet Union and we came face to face with their Air Forces, it became evident for us aviation people that our aircraft technique was superior to the German. Our combat planes were of better design. While sparing no efforts to help our industry rapidly to develop the mass production of new, high-speed fighters, armoured stormoviks and powerful bombers, and striving quickly to put into operation the plants evacuated to the east, Soviet designers constantly sought to improve their airplanes.

EVERYTHING FOR THE FRONT!

As the aircraft industry gained pace and more and more planes were turned out, designers were already working on new improved models.

Their work became more complicated. They had to perfect their machines, to introduce improvements without affecting the daily production quota of planes the plant was sending off to the front.

The designer should always lend an attentive ear to his client. And during the war his client was the front, the airmen who fought in his plane. His task is to correct any flaws detected in time and further to perfect his machine by increasing its speed, range, manoeuvrability and armament.

To be out of touch with life, with the front, is the worst thing that can happen to a designer. A designer must not "fall in love" with his model, he must not think that he has reached the ideal because if he does so he may forget that the enemy also is continuously improving his aircraft.

A good designer must also be a good tactician. He must be well aware of the capabilities of his airplane and give timely advice as to how it can be used most effectively.

The role and responsibility of a designer in war are immensely greater than in time of peace. Not only must he keep a close watch on the enemy's advance in technology but he must also envisage and predict its future development so as always to be one step ahead.

CHAPTER FOUR

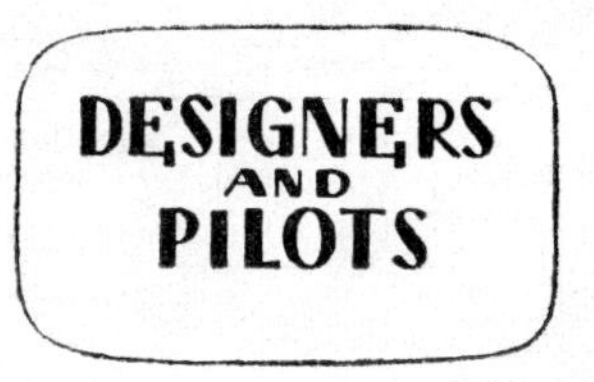

DESIGNERS AND PILOTS

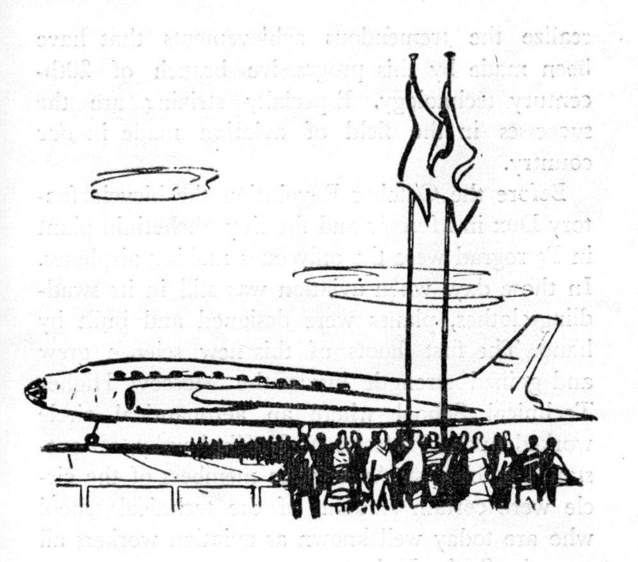

THE FIRST YEARS OF NATIONAL POWER

The history of aviation unfolded before the very eyes of our generation from its birth, from the first timid attempts of "flying bookshelves" to stay in the air at the dawn of aviation till the present day when supersonic aircraft span the continents.

Present-day aviation is only fifty years old. Glancing back at the recent past you come to realize the tremendous achievements that have been made by this progressive branch of 20th-century technology. Especially striking are the successes in the field of aviation made in our country.

Before the October Revolution the bicycle factory Dux in Moscow and the tiny Shchetinin plant in Petrograd were the only ones making airplanes. In those days when aviation was still in its swaddling-clothes, planes were designed and built by hand. The first shoots of this new science grew and gained strength inside the Moscow Higher Technical School where an aeronautical circle worked under Professor N. Y. Zhukovsky, an outstanding scientist. Among the members of the circle were certain students of the technical school who are today well known as aviation workers all over the Soviet Union.

The Soviet Union had to begin building its aviation from the very beginning.

One of the first signs of the young Soviet state's care for its aviation was the Decree of the Council of People's Commissars signed by V. I. Lenin on the establishment of the Central Institute of Aerohydrodynamics under Professor Zhukovsky. This institute later on achieved world importance and became our biggest centre of aviation science.

Soviet people laid the foundations for our powerful aviation in the most trying years of the de-

Sergei Ilyushin

Ilyushin's first glider *Rabfakovets* (1923)

velopment of Soviet power under conditions of foreign intervention and blockade, suffering from hunger and cold. They established their science, built their plants, brought up and trained a whole army of scientists, designers, engineers and workers of the aviation industry.

WITH OUR OWN HANDS

In the 20s we made no bones of making use of planes captured from the intervention troops. However, by 1930 all the basic types of our planes and engines were being built at Soviet plants by Soviet workers and engineers.

The qualitative and quantitative growth of aviation in the period of 1930-35 vividly reflected the upheaval in the entire Soviet national economy. We developed and put into mass production the I-15 and I-16 fighter-planes designed by Polikarpov which were considered first-class at that stage, and the Tupolev bombers, the biggest in the world, first the TB-1 and then the TB-3, as well as the M-11, AM-34, M-62 and M-100 aircraft engines designed by Shvetsov, Mikulin and Klimov.

In the first ten years of its existence the young Soviet aviation emerged into the front rank.

Until the middle of the 30s we had two principal aircraft designing bureaus—Polikarpov's and

Tupolev's—and three engine bureaus—Mikulin's, Klimov's and Shvetsov's.

But already before World War II the Party and the Soviet Government saw to it that their number was increased. The new designing bureaus developed the MiG, La and Yak fighter-planes, Il stormoviks and Pe and Tu bombers.

After the victorious end of the war our first jet planes took part in the fly-past at the Tushino Airfield in the summer of 1946.

Ever since jet aviation has made rapid progress each year.

And remember helicopters. Is it long, I would ask you, since they have established themselves so firmly as part of our life?

If the first light, delicate dragon-flies developed by M. L. Mil created short of sensation, today people take the news of the giant helicopter Yak-24, the "flying wagon," in their stride: "Tut-tut, think of it, one of the biggest of its kind in the world," they say.

WINGS OF OUR COUNTRY

Success did not come easily. The revolutionary advances made became possible not only through the efforts of our designing bureaus but above all through the work of the staff of the Central Institute of Aerohydrodynamics and other research institutions who blazed the trail in aeronautics.

Many well-known scientists who have followed Zhukovsky and Chaplygin and have advanced our aeronautics and contributed to the development of the Soviet aircraft industry, enjoy deserved authority and respect among Soviet aviation workers.

Only a designing bureau staffed by highly-skilled workers and equipped with up-to-date laboratories and test-stands can develop modern aircraft, the most complicated machine of our times, the epitome of science and technology.

The time has long passed when solitary talented inventors built their airplanes at the dawn of aviation in primitive shops.

Today the work of a designer is the most complicated form of creative effort of the whole body of workers. In the past the designer was a lone pioneer, today he is the leader and organizer of a large group of engineers, technicians and workers.

Our designers enjoy the attention and respect of the Soviet people and the invariable help and support of the Party and the Government. The state spares no expense to provide them with the conditions necessary for fruitful work.

Wonderful builders of aircraft, engines and instruments have come to the fore in the course of the advance made in aviation. The designing bureaus of aircraft designers such as Tupolev, Ilyushin, Mikoyan, Myasishchev, Lavochkin, Sukhoi, Antonov and of engine designers such as Klimov, Shvetsov, Mikulin, Lyulka, Tumansky, Kuznetsov are widely known. Each has its own style, its own creative approach, but together they are working towards one common goal: building our Soviet aviation, the wings of our country.

THE FIRST FLYING TANK EVER

From the very first days of my activity as a designer I enjoyed the constant support of Sergei Ilyushin, then a student of the Air Force Academy and today the designer of the first ground-attack aircraft in the history of aviation famous the world over.

Ilyushin was the only aircraft designer in the world who thought of developing a stormovik capable of destroying enemy tanks and troops from the air.

Every airplane sufficiently armed with machine-guns, cannons and bombs can attack tanks but bombs, machine-guns and cannons are most effective if used against ground targets at low heights.

Don't think that tanks are defenceless: they have anti-aircraft machine-guns and guns. Ilyushin thought of what may seem a simple idea, he protected the engine, pilot's cockpit, radiator and other most essential parts of his aircraft with armour plating and actually turned it into a flying tank. The stormovik takes no heed of either rifle or machine-gun fire and only a direct hit from a cannon is dangerous to it.

Many were sceptical: "What on earth is that? Who needs a plane with such a low speed and poor ceiling?"

These short-sighted people could not realize that a stormovik was not a fighter, that its strength was not in its high speed and ceiling but in its cannons, machine-guns and bombs and most of all in its armour which made it possible to use it against enemy tanks at low height.

The government expressed a high opinion of the aircraft and it was turned out in great quantities.

SERGEI ILYUSHIN'S LIFE PATH

Ilyushin's path to fame and success was not an easy one.

During the first Aviation Week held in Petersburg in 1913 Ilyushin was an unskilled hand clearing and levelling the airfield.

In 1914 he was called up to the army. He served at the Petersburg airfield as an airfield ground crew hand, then a mechanic and finally became a pilot.

During the Civil War Ilyushin was already in charge of an aircraft repair train which was transferred from one front to another.

In the 30s he developed his bomber the Il-4. The first model of this aircraft met with misfortune. When already in mass production a serious flaw was discovered in the oil-radiator system: the engine was subject to overheating.

In time this shortcoming could have been easily eliminated if calm consideration had been given to the problem. But the atmosphere at the plant was very unhealthy. Ilyushin was rebuked for having overlooked the flaw in the cooling system and for having approved the mass production of a faulty aircraft. Ill-wishers began to guestion all Ilyushin's work. Ilyushin took these attacks to heart.

When the Government learned of the incident they took Ilyushin's side and helped to clear up the atmosphere at the plant. Ilyushin eliminated the shortcomings and very soon Ils began to roll off the line in batches. The aircraft showed a high flying performance. In one airplane of the type specially equipped for the purpose Vladimir Kokkinaki, a well-known test pilot, made a non-stop flight from Moscow to the U.S.A. across the North Atlantic.

Sergei Ilyushin worked along with other designers in the field of high-speed aircraft.

Today at fly-pasts we watch Ilyushin's jet bombers with a feeling of admiration and pride in our Soviet aviation.

Ilyushin's passenger planes the Il-12 and Il-14 visited practically every corner of the globe. His recent creation is a first-class giant liner the *Moskva* Il-18 equipped with four turbo-prop engines.

AN ACCIDENT

I remember an accident which gave me a bad turn once. In 1935 we built a three-seater liaison plane. It was very sleek in appearance, comfortable inside and had extremely simple controls. The airplane entered for the sporting flight Sevastopol-Moscow and won the prize.

Ilyushin took to it the moment he saw this small craft. At that time his machines were being built outside Moscow and he often had to fly to the plant and back. He used a slow Po-2 and wasted a lot of time. He begged us to give him the plane and we readily consented.

When Sergei Ilyushin came to Moscow he thanked us for the plane each time he saw us. One evening Raivicher, the airfield commander, phoned me up and said:

"We have just been informed that Ilyushin has had a crash on his way to Moscow in some red plane or other. Isn't that your plane?"

Yes, the airplane which I had given to Ilyushin was a red one.

I was horrified. Ilyushin had a crack-up. What had happened? I could not sit still. At last good news came: the plane had crashed but the pilot was alive.

I saw Ilyushin a few days later. His head was swathed in bandages. I hugged my friend with great relief.

"Alexander," he said. "I have no grudge against you. The craft is wonderful, but it turned out, that the engine cannot operate without oil. One mustn't overlook this small detail."

His engine had failed in the air because there was no oil in the system. It was the mechanic's fault—he had forgotten to replenish the engine oil. Ilyushin had had to make a forced landing in the darkness in unknown country. A scar across his forehead would always remind Sergei Ilyushin of this accident.

THE HEART OF AN AIRCRAFT

The names of Soviet aircraft designers are very well known in our country, especially after the Government took the decision to give fighters, stormoviks, bombers, transport and training planes the names of their designers.

But we must not forget the designers of aircraft engines. It is they who give life to an aircraft, because the engine is the heart of an aircraft.

I would like to tell you about a man who greatly contributed to the success of our aviation.

The man is Vladimir Yakovlevich Klimov. His name is linked with all the achievements of our Soviet aviation in the field of piston and jet engines.

My own work is closely interwoven with the activities of Vladimir Klimov, one of the oldest Russian aircraft-engine designers. His engine, the M-105 which during the war was given the name of VK-105 (short for Vladimir Klimov), was installed in our fighter-planes.

Though extremely grim and unapproachable in appearance, Vladimir was the most charming person and the kindest friend I ever knew.

When developing the new model of a fighter-plane I worked in close co-operation with Klimov, trying to ensure that his engine had the most favourable conditions to develop its best performance in the future plane.

The task of an aircraft designer is to convert the power of an engine into speed, manoeuvrability and flight ceiling. The designer's art is skilfully to combine the work of an engine with that of an aircraft. Klimov is well aware of this and I on my side try not to forget it for a moment. The result of our efforts were fast, highly manoeuvrable fighters with great fire-power.

KLIMOV'S KEEN THOUGHT

Klimov was one of the first designers in the world who came to understand the importance of arming fighters with cannons and who spared no effort in achieving this idea.

Vladimir Klimov integrated the cannon in the engine. Its barrel was inserted into the hollow propeller shaft with the cannon firing through the propeller hub without damaging the blades when the engine was operating.

Vladimir Klimov's outstanding achievement allowed Soviet aircraft designers to mount large calibre cannons in their fighters.

In addition fighters have cannons and machine-guns of smaller calibre firing through the propeller blades. They are called synchronized guns—that is, they have a device by which the guns cannot fire when a propeller blade is in front of the muzzle.

The work of Vladimir Klimov is inseparably linked with the development of Soviet aviation. He developed an 800 h.p. engine for the pre-war Tupolev bomber CB. His 1,000 h.p. M-105 engines powered Pe-2 bombers widely used during the war. Finally his 1,200 h.p. water-cooled engines were mounted in fighter-planes which got the better of and finally completely suppressed Nazi fighters and bombers.

Vladimir Klimov played an important part in creating the first Soviet-made jet engines which were mounted in supersonic swept-wing fighters MiG.

On his 60th birthday the Government awarded Vladimir Klimov with his fifth Order of Lenin for his services in building up the country's air-power.

ARTEM MIKOYAN COMES TO AVIATION

If you ask anyone of our leading aircraft designers how he came to fall in love with aviation and became a designer they will all have practically the same thing to tell you. It all began, they will say, with a crack or a peep-hole in an airfield fence through which they made their first acquaintance with aviation.

It happened with me and it happened with most of our designers.

Artem Mikoyan was an exception to the rule. He came to aviation without that initial stage in most designers' education.

Born in 1906 in a Caucasian mountain village in Armenia, where there were no fences to hide planes from view, Artem made his acquaintance with aviation after graduating from school and from the Air Force Academy.

He became a true aviator in 1933 when he answered the call of the Air Force Commander-in-Chief Yakov Alksnis for volunteers to make parachute jumps. He, then a secretary of the first course at the Academy, stepped out from the ranks. Parachute-jumping was in its infancy in our country, the ground was unexplored and people looked upon the whole business with caution.

"Naturally I was scared stiff," he said to a friend many years after his jump. "But everything went without a hitch." Today Mikoyan is the only one of the leading Soviet designers who has the right to wear a parachutist's badge in his lapel.

MUTUAL HELP AND THE COMPETITIVE SPIRIT

Artem Mikoyan started out in aircraft designing together with Mikhail Gurevich under Polikarpov, one of the oldest Soviet designers.

They were quick in showing their worth and were soon given designing work on their own.

MiG fighters attracted attention at the beginning of the Great Patriotic War. MiG stands for Mikoyan and Gurevich. Their MiG-15 became world famous. It can be said without exaggeration that it was the best immediate post-war jet fighter in the world.

Artem Mikoyan is a thickset, swarthy man with jet-black, curly hair and a smiling face always full of vitality. His speech is lively with a slight Caucasian accent and sparkles with wit. Firm comrades, we would share opinions and help each other to solve complicated problems.

Semyon Lavochkin is another designer who works in the field of fighter-plane designing.

Occasionally Lavochkin, Mikoyan and I would get one and the same order and then our bureaus would get down to work and compete with each other: who would come up first with the finished design, whose design would be better, whose model would be accepted by the Air Force. And if we "beat" each other in this competition, the winner is our common cause.

ANDREI TUPOLEV WATCHES A FLIGHT

Once, when I was still a mechanic at the Moscow Central Airfield, I was pottering about with a carburettor, when a fellow-worker came running into the shop.

"Want to see Tupolev? Come on."

"Tupolev? Lead me on."

We saw people crowding around a silver-winged beauty of a plane standing on the tarmac. It was an all-metal job with its plating made of ribbed duralumin.

The mechanic and his assistants were bustling about the engine and we saw Mikhail Gromov, a test pilot, sitting in the cockpit at the controls. Final instructions were given to the pilot and good-byes said. The engine roared and the plane rolled out to the starting line. At that moment a man detached himself from the group of engineers and mechanics, walked a few steps forward and stood there watching the plane. He remained alone all through the flight and no one made any attempt to approach him or to disturb his state of excited emotion.

That was how we first met Andrei Nikolayevich Tupolev who had come to see his new plane being flight-tested. It seemed that at that moment he did not feel the ground under his feet, that he was in the air, in the pilot's cockpit.

Andrei Tupolev is the oldest of all our designers but he is still bubbling with energy. Although seventy, he is still working hard and is cheerful and lively as a youth. There is always a smile on his face. He is a very simple, sociable man who enjoys a hearty laugh once in a while which is the envy of many of us of the "younger" generation.

Tupolev is a worker of wide scope in engineering. In the 30s he put a lot of energy and effort as Chief Engineer of the Aviation Industry Administration into building large aircraft factories while continuing his full-scale designing activities. He took an interest in and wanted to see everything with his own eyes. Although extremely busy he found time to come to the Tushino Airfield and to the Dynamo Acquatic Station at Khimki to be present at the test-flights of my new sports planes —the UT-1, UT-2 and others.

In those days I was a young designer and my conversations with him and his critical remarks meant a lot to me.

ZHUKOVSKY'S STUDENT

Tupolev's name is inseparably linked with the construction of the Central Institute of Aerohydrodynamics which was begun in 1919 on the site of the former German settlement in Moscow near the Lutheran church where, as the legend goes, Peter the Great sat with his friend Yakov Bruss, an astronomer and mathematician, sipping beer and smoking his pipe. Tupolev, Arkhangelsky, Ushakov, Musinyants, Yuriev, Vetchinkin and other well-known aircraft designers and celebrated scientists of today, who were then young, budding engineers, and former students of the Moscow Higher Technical School and Moscow University, took an active part in organizing the work of this research centre. They were directed by Nikolai Zhukovsky, the father of Russian aviation, and by his associate, Sergei Chaplygin, who later became an academician.

The biggest research institute for those times, it was completed with modern equipment in a very brief span of time owing to very strong governmental support. Since then the institute has become the test laboratory for every Soviet designer. Airplane models undergo rigid tests in wind-tunnels so that the designer can check numerous variations of a future aircraft under laboratory conditions and pick out the best, thus ensuring the highest speed, stability and control.

Gradually Andrei Tupolev, one of Zhukovsky's most capable students, became the heart and soul of the new institute. An experimental plant was established at the institute along with laboratories, wind-tunnels and test-rigs where first Soviet planes were designed and built under the direction of Andrei Tupolev.

A HOST OF PLANES

Tupolev initiated all-metal aircraft in the Soviet Union. If you discount his first attempts in aviation—light sports planes, equipped with engines of foreign make—his ANT-3 with a Soviet-made 400 h.p. engine was already a full-fledged all-metal aircraft. It was adopted in the Red Air Force as the reconnaissance plane, R-3. In this aircraft the pilot Gromov and his flight engineer Rodzevich made their first international flight across Europe.

Tupolev's firstling (1923). The designer is in the centre

Vladimir Kokkinaki

This aircraft, named *Proletary*, made quite a stir abroad.

ANT-3 was followed by a three-engine passenger plane ANT-9. It was a large plane and its European flight piloted by the same Gromov created a sensation.

Every year Tupolev came up with a new design.

The flights of Chkalov, Baidukov and Belyakov and later of Gromov, Yumashev and Danilin from Moscow to America across the North Pole accomplished in Tupolev's ANT-25 or RD (stands for record range), equipped with an AM-34 engine designed by Alexander Mikulin, brought our aviation world renown. It was a virtual triumph for our pilots, for the whole Soviet aircraft industry which had produced the ANT-25 and its AM-34 engine entirely from Soviet-made materials at Soviet plants with the hands of Soviet workers and from drawings made by Soviet engineers. The ANT-25 was the twenty-fifth aircraft designed by Andrei Tupolev.

Towards the end of the war a twin-engine bomber was very popular with our Soviet pilots. In post-war years Tupolev developed a number of new airplanes with TU-104 and TU-114 standing out among them.

Standing out on the green carpet of the airfield is a new airplane, its fresh coat of paint sparkling in the sun, its metal parts gleaming. Soon it will be taken up into the air and flight-tested at various altitudes and speeds to prove the soundness of the designer's concepts.

The first man to put the new craft through its paces will be the test pilot.

In my opinion there is no other profession among aviators more noble, lofty and heroic than that of a test pilot.

The modern science of aeronautics is a powerful weapon in the hands of an aircraft designer. Nevertheless, the first flights of a new aircraft are fraught with many unexpected developments. The task of a test pilot is to reveal all the intricacies which elude the designer when he does his calculations on the machine and when the experimental model undergoes static tests.

It is not so much the very first flight that is dangerous as the following flights when the machine is tested for maximum speed, ceiling, airworthiness, flutter and spin. The test pilot keeps a careful track of the airplane's behaviour and is on his toes until the machine is known and sized up in every aspect.

It is not for nothing that pilots say you cannot

afford to be chummy with a new plane too soon.

I have met quite a few outstanding men in this profession: Chkalov and Piontkovsky, Fedrovi and Anokhin, Serov and Kokkinaki, Suprun and Gromov. Each with his own vividly pronounced individuality, they were all characterized by one trait —a profound and striking love for aviation. The constant danger of test flights had left its imprint on these people: they are all characterized by an unusual manly modesty and by an unassumed cheerfulness.

Mikhail Gromov is our most modest and also our most experienced test pilot.

GROMOV THE WIZARD

I saw Gromov for the first time on a bright summer morning in 1926 at the Central Airfield. A new U-2 was being wheeled out of the hangar in preparation for its maiden flight. Nikolai Polikarpov, the designer, was briefing Mikhail Gromov by his first-born plane. Gromov, already in a flying suit, was unhurriedly and confidently preparing for the flight: straightening his helmet, rubbing his goggles, attentively listening to the designer.

Polikarpov, a stocky, thickset man with an open, Russian face and lively eyes, was evidently nervous. To relieve his tension he tried to joke.

Patting the wing of the airplane tenderly, as if he was a merchant offering his wares, and nodding at the low-powered engine (an M-11), he smiled: "Some engine that. It's got dog's power in it not horse's."

Gromov climbed inside the cockpit and started the motor.

"Good luck, there!"

A few minutes later the U-2 was in the air.

The U-2 which Gromov flight-tested on that morning and which was later called the Po-2 after its designer was one of the mass-produced and popular airplanes. Thousands and thousands of reliable Po-2s faithfully served in every corner of our country for several scores of years. During the war these ungainly planes lent army boys a helping hand harassing the enemy in his front-line trenches.

Gromov's range of flying qualification is hard to grasp: from the first test flights in the smallest craft in the world, a U-2, to the *Maxim Gorky*, the world's biggest airplane in those days.

Heavy aircraft building in our country is directly connected with the outstanding activities of Mikhail Gromov. He gave a start in life to the Tupolev bombers which served in the Air Force for a long period.

PILOT NUMBER ONE

Mikhail Gromov is tall, lean, and at first glance, you might say, a bit dull. But appearances are deceptive. He is a mild and sensitive person, a sportsman from head to foot with a boyish flare for all kinds of sports and especially riding horses.

Gromov's sporting spirit permeates his activity as an airman. It was Gromov and his flight engineer Rodzevich who astonished Europe by the round trip in the first Soviet-made all-metal plane *Proletary*. It was Gromov who took a three-engine ANT-9 on a flight round the European capitals which aroused respect for Soviet aviation.

It was Gromov who with Rodzevich made an outstanding Moscow-Peking flight in a R-1 plane equipped with a Soviet M-5 engine.

And finally it was Gromov who, practically at the same time as Chkalov, made his dramatic flight from the Soviet Union to the United States of America across the North Pole in an ANT-25 and became the glory of Russian aviation and a world celebrity.

After this flight the Americans called Gromov Pilot No. 1.

During pre-war years Mikhail Gromov was the head of the Test-Flight Research Centre and in 1941 he obtained permission to be sent to the front where he was in command of a large Air Force formation throughout the war. In the post-war years he headed the aircraft industry test-flight service.

Colonel-general Gromov's heroic deeds are recorded in the history of the creation and development of Soviet aviation. Today he is writing a book of recollections which will be of great interest to the younger generation of Soviet airmen.

SERGEI ANOKHIN, HERO OF THE SOVIET UNION

I have known Sergei Anokhin, parachutist, gliderman, sporting pilot, record-holder and test pilot of the latest jet aircraft for many years. But I will never stop admiring his unusual skill, his incredible airmanship.

Sergei is a slender, spare, almost fragile, man. A strip of black cloth covers one socket. This modest and shy man volunteered to build up wing-load in flight to the point of destruction in order to test the airworthiness of a new plane, to check actual loads acting upon its frame during aerobatics, and compare them with the mathematically calculated theoretical loads.

He deliberately and willingly agreed to carry out this task, realizing only too well the dangers such a flight spelt for him. He went up and deliberately destroyed the plane in the air providing valuable data for aeronautics, for the calculations of the airworthiness of the newly designed aircraft.

At high altitude Anokhin bailed out of the plane which was shattered to pieces and came safely down on a parachute, but this experiment had cost him his left eye.

One of our designing bureaus developed a pilotless guided missile. To speed up the trials the designers wished to put a pilot inside the missile for the first test flights to adjust its controls and check its stability.

Again it was Anokhin who volunteered to fly in the missile and guide it with the help of special controls which would simulate radio control. Sergei saw the missile through its tests with great skill and thanks to him our country was soon in possession of a new and formidable weapon.

I do not remember a single instance of his shirking any task, however complicated and dangerous.

When he accepted such offers he always said:

"Well, let's give it a try." Then after a moment's silence he would add: "Yes, I'll give it a try. I think everything will be all right."

After completing his test programme and flying at tremendous heights with fabulous speeds, calm and imperturbable, he would report the results of the flights in an even voice as if he had been doing his usual, everyday work:

"Well, everything's all right," and then he would jot down his impressions of the plane on the test card.

THE CRUCIAL MOMENT

One day Anokhin went up to test a new plane. His voice came over the radio:

"Everything's all right, I'm at 33,000 feet."

"Everything's all right, I'm at 48,000. . . ."

"Fifty thousand, levelling out. . . ."

"Switching on the afterburner. Speed mounts rapidly. . . ."

"Stick force increases. . . ."

"Hard to maintain horizontal attitude. . . ."

Then silence. Why? Why is it "hard to maintain"? We are at a loss.

Tension mounts. What has happened to the plane and the pilot? Why is he silent? We are tormented by these questions until someone from the ground crew rushes into the CP and cries happily:

"Coming in for the landing!"

When we reach the starting line, the plane is already there. We look at the calm, imperturbable man in the cockpit and feel fine.

Anokhin climbs out of the plane and explains in a business-like tone:

"As soon as I said, 'Hard to maintain horizontal attitude,' my radio broke down. At the most interesting moment, I should say."

That's how it happens sometimes.

Every day way up there beyond the clouds Sergei Anokhin, Hero of the Soviet Union, a wonderful test pilot, emerges victorious from single combat with a capricious and highly complicated machine.

A YOUTHFUL PILOT—PAVEL FEDROVI

At the 1925 Glider Competitions in Koktebel I was introduced to a lean, dark-haired young man in a military airman's uniform.

"Meet Pavel Fedrovi, the pilot who will test your glider."

I was somewhat taken aback by the youthfulness of the pilot who was to test my glider. Compared with such flying past masters as Artseulov, Yungmeister, Kudrin and others he did not inspire faith. The pilots treated him with a patronizing air and called him simply Pasha. Some even called him Pashka the Gypsy because of his swarthiness. But nothing could be done about it: he was assigned to me, and I had to acquaint him with the glider and arrange details of our flights.

At last all the preliminaries were over. Just before the flight, still assailed by doubts as to Pasha's qualifications, I asked him what planes he had flown. He answered dashingly and without hesitation: "'What planes,' you ask? All kinds. Except foreign makes, of course," he added.

I would have felt better if I had not asked him

that confounded question. His answer gave me a jar. For in 1925 we had no planes of our own and all the pilots flew old captured machines.

But it was too late. The glider was already at the starting line, the ground crew were getting the lines ready and Fedrovi was buckling himself to the seat in the cockpit.

"All set. Let her go!" shouted Pasha.

The shock-absorber lines were stretched to their fullest extent. The wave-off man signalled with his flag, the glider rolled over the ground, became airborne, flew for a bit, then, its tail wobbling, the glider banked, hit the ground with its right strut and, with its wing ploughing the ground, swerved sharply and landed on its belly, its struts crippled.

"I knew it!" I cried in despair running up to the sprawling glider, ready to give the unfortunate test pilot a sound thrashing. "You call yourself a pilot, you're nothing but a bungler!" I could hardly hold back my tears.

"Well, it happens sometimes," Pasha said. "Don't you worry. Fix up the struts and we shall try once more."

It did not take long to put the struts back into shape again and other pilots later made several successful flights in the glider. But you will easily understand that Pasha did not have another chance to fly in it.

I would have never believed it if I had been

told that fifteen years later, shortly before the war, a new chief test pilot would be appointed to our designing bureau and that this new pilot would be Pasha Fedrovi.

GENERAL PAVEL FEDROVI

Yet this was exactly what happened. This was no longer the youth we had known before. It was a distinguished, courageous, professional test pilot with tremendous experience, a past master of his trade, a man who was respected by all, whose chest was decorated with rows of ribbons and who was a General into the bargain.

But Pasha remained just as jovial, frank and good company as in his youthful days. I was sometimes astounded by his ability to strike up an acquaintanceship.

The following incident invariably brings a smile to my lips.

Once at the end of the war Pasha and I boarded a train bound for Leningrad. The train had hardly pulled out of the station when Pasha stepped out of our compartment into the passage and immediately I heard him talking animatedly with someone. "Must be some friend of his," I thought.

Pasha reappeared accompanied by a man whose face seemed very familiar to me. And before I realized that it was Arkady Raikin, a well-known artist, Pasha pushed the embarrassed Raikin towards me saying:

"Arkady, meet the designer."

When Raikin left I turned to Pasha:

"I didn't know you were friends."

"Friends?"

"Didn't you call him by his first name?"

"What else can I call him by? I don't even know his patronymics. This is the first time I have ever met him."

During the four war years Pasha was responsible for the test flights of all the fighters produced by our plant. Time and again he would risk his life during experimental flights perfecting new models of fighter-planes for the Air Force.

We put out about thirty thousand Yak-1, Yak-3, Yak-7 and Yak-9s, the first experimental models of which passed through the hands of General Pavel Fedrovi.

MOSCOW-AMERICA VIA THE NORTH POLE

In July 1936 the whole country learned some amazing news: On July 20-22 pilot Valery Chkalov, co-pilot Georgy Baidukov and navigator Alexander Belyakov made a flight unprecedented in the history of Soviet aviation, the long-range, non-stop flight from Moscow to Nikolayevsk-on-Amur, a total of 9,374 km. The plane was airborne for 56 hours 20 minutes.

One year later they amazed the entire world by a new non-stop flight to the United States of America, having covered over 12,000 km. from Moscow to the Vancouver airfield near Portland, Oregon, on the Pacific seaboard, in 63 hours 25 minutes. The trio crossed the then unexplored North Pole linking two world's major states by the shortest possible route: Moscow—White Sea—Barents Sea—Novaya Zemlya—North Pole—Patrick Isle—Pirce Point in North Canada and the state of Washington in the U.S.A.

The front pages of newspapers all over the world gave the flight big headlines.

"Fantastic non-stop flight. Three Russians over North Pole!"

"The North Pole is conquered! Outstanding event in aviation history!"

Adorned with garlands Chkalov and his comrades slowly made their way through streets of Portland strewn with flowers.

The *New York World Telegram* wrote in its editorial that the presence of mind with which they had carried through their dangerous mission, the precision with which they had stuck to their difficult course could not but evoke admiration of a courage and audacity which knew no obstacles.

Chkalov was our hero then. His coolness, precision and courage became the symbol of "the Chkalov style" in aviation.

The wonderful flights accomplished by Chkalov and his comrades were a national triumph for our country. I was lucky to know Chkalov in person and to witness his everyday arduous work as a test pilot, a job which very often requires no less presence of mind, precision and courage than the flight across the North Pole.

VALERY CHKALOV

I met Valery Chkalov for the first time in 1931 at an aircraft plant to which I was assigned after graduating from the Air Force Academy. At that time he was an ordinary pilot and his glory came years later. When I was introduced to him, I only knew that he was a most charming person and a very reckless pilot: all sorts of legends about Chkalov's dare-devil flights were already in circulation by then.

There were stories of Valery Chkalov flying an airplane under the Nikolaevsky Bridge span on the Neva River in Leningrad.

Or of an incident which occurred during the testing of a new plane. Chkalov was about to land when he discovered that one of the struts had got stuck and would not lower. Chkalov performed numerous barrel rolls over the airfield followed by a cascade of dizzy acrobatics until finally he managed to force the strut out and came down safely.

At the plant Chkalov rightly enjoyed the reputation of being a person who possessed all the qualities necessary for the intricate job of testing new planes. He was always striving to "fathom the soul of a new plane," as he used to say, more fully, more quickly and more thoroughly.

Thickset, stocky and broad as a barrel, Chkalov was always straightforward, with a deep rich voice betraying a native of the Volga countryside. You could never be dull when he was there, with his long, amusing stories of his flying experience, of which he had an inexhaustible fund.

HIS PRESENCE OF MIND

My old friend, Yulian Piontkovsky, who also worked at the plant as test pilot, introduced me to Valery. Unlike the jovial and lively Chkalov, Piontkovsky was slow and short-spoken although he too could enjoy a good joke. Completely different on the surface, these two, nevertheless, had much in common: their attitude towards their profession full of risks but at the same time wonderful and noble.

We often visited the Dynamo restaurant and exchanged jokes over our lunch. The pilots would launch into their reminiscences: Chkalov would talk about his flying school and his service in the Air Force and Piontkovsky of his exploits in the Civil War and of his flights in captured "coffins."

Once Piontkovsky and an observer went on a sortie in an old two-seater Sopwith. Some time later his detachment commander received a telegram from him reading: "Flew in. Got stuck. Dispatch flat-car."

This telegram should be deciphered as follows: Engine failed. Had to bellyland in a bog. Plane is damaged.

"Some flights," Piontkovsky continued. "But we were not easily put off."

Chkalov would remember one of his stories. There would be more jokes and Chkalov would laugh loudest of all. An hour later the pilots would take their places in the cockpits of new planes ready to start their risky test flights. There was not a trace of anxiety in them, neither in their voices, nor in their movements, nor in their eyes. They puzzled me and I tried in vain to make them out, to find the answer to their apparent devil-may-care attitude. As time went by I understood that it could not be otherwise. If a pilot loses his equilibrium, his confidence in himself and in his ability, he will never be able to control a new and perhaps refractory machine. If he does lose this sense of calm, it means that the time has come for him to end his career as a test pilot.

Valery Chkalov

Vladimir Klimov

CANNOT HELP BEING WORRIED

A test pilot is the designer's best assistant in creating a new aircraft.

The designer, although he is not a pilot, must know all the intricacies of the plane's behaviour in the air.

It is very important that there should be complete understanding between the designer and the test pilot. They must speak common language and both be quick in the uptake. Chkalov possessed a wonderful ability in fathoming a plane's temperament.

A test pilot is a cool customer but I cannot give the designers the same credit.

The latest model goes up into the air piloted by a past master such as Chkalov. It seems that there is nothing to be worried about.

The plane has been designed by experienced engineers. It has been calculated and checked down to the minutest detail. It seems that everything has been done to make the test flight safe and to ensure its success.

What is more, the designer is well aware of it, more than anybody else, but still....

It is hard to compare the emotion experienced by the designer during the few minutes of the first flight of a new craft with any other feeling.

Back in Chkalov's days the minutes of waiting

were even more agonizing because there was no radio communication between the pilot and the ground and as the plane vanished from sight we were completely at a loss as to its fate until the end of the flight.

Even one minute's delay by a plane due to return from a test flight is enough to raise your blood pressure. Your pulse quickens and you begin to imagine all sorts of things: what if something has gone wrong with the plane. And then the aircraft with your friend is safely back at the airfield and you feel as if a burden has been lifted from your shoulders. This anxiety is familiar, I think, to every designer.

ALEXANDER YERSHOV'S ANSWER

Our test pilots put planes through their paces after their birth, as it were, deep in the rear at the plant's airfield. Subsequently these airplanes underwent further extensive trials in combat at the front-line airfields in the hands of fighting airmen. We waited impatiently for letters from the front telling us how the pilots fought in the air in our fighters.

In the course of the war we received numerous pointers and much advice which helped us to make a number of major improvements in our machines.

I once got a letter describing the deeds of the pilot Yershov:

"Lieutenant Alexander Yershov has seen only one month of combat flying in his Yak-3. During this month he had six air engagements and knocked down ten enemy planes. Once eight of our fighters were attacked by thirty Focke-Wulfs. Yershov sliced the fin off one of the Fockes with the wing of his fighter and shot down one more with his machine-gun and cannon fire. The next day he and another pilot encountered sixteen Focke-Wulfs. A dog-fight ensued in which he added another three enemy fighters to his account."

I was very glad to hear of Yershov's successes and sent him a telegram of congratulations. Some time later I received an answer which moved me deeply. After informing me that he had shot down another five enemy planes Yershov went on to speak about himself:

"I am twenty-two, but I started to fly back in 1938. Four years as a flying instructor helped me to squeeze maximum efficiency out of the Yak-3. Ever since my childhood, when I liked to read books about aviation, I dreamed of becoming a real test pilot. I'm sure you have among your drawings designs for planes which I'm only dreaming of."

A few years after the end of the war I learned that Alexander Yershov had seen the war through and that the dream of his boyhood had come true: he had become a test pilot.

WHAT FRONT-LINE AIRMEN WROTE

In 1943 a letter came from a group of airmen in a Guards unit with a request to send "four planes of the latest design to make it hot for the vaunted German Messerschmitt fighters."

To back up their request the authors of the letter wrote:

"Here is our combat record:

"1. Captain of the Guards Gorbunov. In action from August 1942. Has 19 enemy planes to his credit, out of which 15 Messerschmitt fighters including all kinds of modified models. He also pioneered vertical manoeuvre fighting against Messerschmitts in a Yak-1. This experience has been written up in the papers more than once.

"2. Senior Lieutenant of the Guards Kankoshev. In action from March 1943. Has 12 enemy planes to his credit, 10 of which are Messerschmitt fighters.

"3. Senior Lieutenant of the Guards Pavlov. In action from August 1941. Has shot down 15 enemy planes, 14 of which are Messerschmitts.

"4. Senior Lieutenant of the Guards Kalugin. In action from August 1941. His score is 15 enemy planes, out of which 11 are Messerschmitt fighters."

In my files I have a letter dated March 28, 1945:

"At the Berlin approaches the sky is under our control. I'm sending you a photo of one ordinary

Sergei Anokhin and his wife Margarita Ratsenskaya, a well-known gliderwoman

Vladimir Lavrinenkov

pair: Velichko and Andrienko who in a seven-minute engagement in Yak-3s knocked down before my very eyes four out of eight enemy Fockes. Similar cases are numerous among our airmen.

"Major-General Dzusov."

The workers and employees of the aircraft plants producing the Yak-1, Yak-3, and Yak-9s were glad to receive good news from the front. We designers and the chief engineer of the Yak-3 fighter Konstantin Sinelshchikov were also triumphant: Soviet aircraft construction had got the upper hand. But not even for a moment did we forget that this victory was won primarily by rank-and-file Soviet airmen. Our air supremacy was won by their stamina and valour.

Who was, for example, Alexander Yershov, who had shot down ten enemy planes in a month? A modest young flier, a Muscovite, a former student at a flying club.

TWO ENCOUNTERS WITH VLADIMIR LAVRINENKOV

I frequently met front-line airmen. I remember a telephone call that came once from a Chief Marshall of the Air Force with a request to issue one fighter-plane to Lavrinenkov, Hero of the Soviet Union and a wonderful pilot. On the next day Lavrinenkov entered my office and stood to attention reporting—I was a General and he a Senior Lieutenant. I walked from behind the desk and begged him to sit down. I looked at this stocky, swarthy lad with his closely-cropped head with respect: a young man, almost a boy, modest and bashful. I had some difficulty in making him overcome his shyness, feel at ease and start telling me about himself and about his combat sorties in Yaks.

After that he accepted his new Yak and took off for the front.

A few months later I learned that in one of the fights Lavrinenkov, having spent all his ammunition, had rammed a German Focke-Wulf-190, damaged his plane and had to bail out. He was taken prisoner and brought in for interrogation. At the enemy HQ they learned from his papers that he was a Hero of the Soviet Union.

"What are you fighting for?" A German officer asked him.

"For my country," Lavrinenkov answered.

"And who do you think is going to win?"

"We are."

"Why do you think so?"

"Everyone in my country thinks so. The whole people thinks so," answered Lavrinenkov and refused to answer further questions.

They sent him off to Berlin, for further questioning.

He was taken in a train and closely guarded. Nevertheless, seizing his chance at night, he jumped out of the window of the speeding train. Having recovered from the shock of his fall, he got up and soon realized that he was on Soviet soil occupied by the Germans. Russian people found him, hid him from the Germans and helped him to get in touch with a partisan detachment. Lavrinenkov became a partisan: he blew up bridges, ambushed enemy units and trains, until the partisans joined up with Soviet Army units.

I saw Lavrinenkov once more. This time his chest was adorned with a second gold star of Hero of the Soviet Union.

We designers knew that our planes were a formidable weapon in the hands of such pilots.

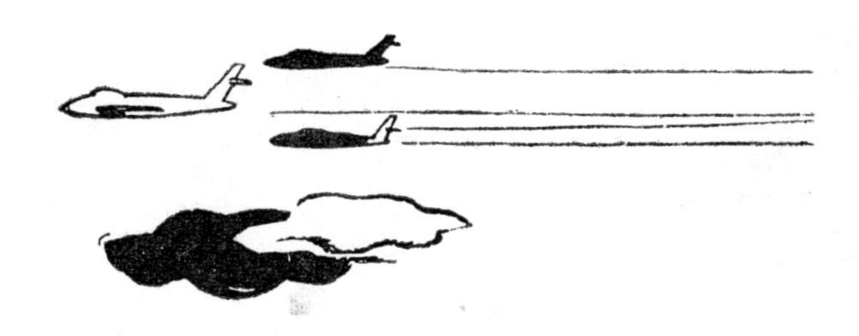

CHAPTER FIVE

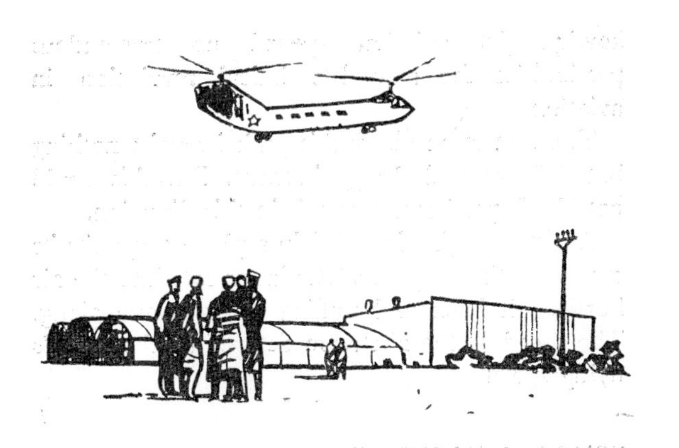

REVOLUTION IN AVIATION

In the 30s it became evident that the conventional type of plane with its piston engine driving a propeller was reaching the limit of its capabilities. After nearly half a century, it had exhausted itself as regards future progress.

In their efforts to increase combat planes' speed and altitude scientists and designers sought new ways in the development of aviation.

And the new way was found: the era of jet aviation arrived. This had been prophesied long ago by our famous countryman Konstantin Tsiolkovsky. Jet aviation opened up tremendous possibilities for a real technical revolution in aviation.

The first steps along this path brought nothing but failures and disappointment. But this could not check persistent research in this direction.

A piston engine installed in a plane transmits its energy to the propeller. The latter eats into the air hurtling it back and pulling the airplane along. The speed of the airstream determines the plane's flying speed.

WHAT IS A JET ENGINE?

To increase the speed, designers concentrated on increasing the power of the engine. But already at a speed of 700 k.p.h. further power increment no matter how great resulted in a very little increase in speed. Greater weight and dimensions of the piston engine and propellers entailed greater gross weight of the plane, increased its drag and all this swallowed up practically the entire power increment of the engine.

It was a dead-end and the jet engine offered a way out. A jet engine has tremendous advantages over a piston one. Although of small weight and size, it can develop enormous thrust transmitting its energy directly to the plane without the help of a heavy and bulky propeller.

Artem Mikoyan

Mikhail Gromov

In a jet engine air is forced by an air compressor into the combustion chamber and then through a turbine (which rotates the compressor) it escapes out of an exhaust nozzle with tremendous speed into the atmosphere thus developing the reactive force which drives the plane forward. The more fuel burns up in the air-jet the more powerful it is and the greater is the speed of the plane. Such is the turbo-jet engine.

There is another type of jet engine, the so-called liquid-fuel jet engine. Just as the turbo-jet engine, it operates on kerosene which is oxydized during burning not by air forced in by a compressor but by some other oxydizer, liquid oxygen or nitric acid, stored in the aircraft in a special tank.

Intensive research and designing work in jet-engine development was in progress in the second half of the 30s in the U.S.S.R., England, Germany, Italy and somewhat later in the United States. In 1938-39 jet engines were developed in Germany by BMW and Junkers companies, in England by Frank A. Whittle and in Italy by Campini-Caproni. The first experimental jet engines, although far from perfect, could already be installed in planes specially built for jet-powered flight.

EARLY DEVELOPMENTS OF THE ITALIANS AND GERMANS

The Italian designers Caproni and Campini built the jet planes CC-1 and CC-2, which made several flights in 1940-41, and on December 1, 1941 accomplished a flight from Milan to Rome. The fuselage of Campini-Caproni airplane was one big pipe from nose to tail. The air entered a round nose intake, then was forced into a two-stage compressor and escaped through a nozzle in the tail with vastly increased velocity and temperature.

Messerschmitt began to work on his Me-262 before the war and the first flight took place in 1942. The plane went through a series of tests in 1942-43 and was then put into mass production.

Parallel with this craft the Messerschmitt company also developed a tailless Me-163 fighter with a liquid jet engine.

Insignificant numbers of Me-163s and Me-262s appeared at the front, but this German "new weapon," like the Heinkel He-162 jet plane, came too late to influence in any way the course of the war.

The first jet-powered flights caused the Germans a lot of trouble, ending in a whole series of crashes.

These crashes could be explained not so much by the novelty of the jet-propelled planes as by the feverish haste with which the Nazi rulers gave the order to begin mass production of new machines which had been hurriedly and insufficiently tested, so as to bring them into play at the front as quickly as possible. Inevitable in such cases crack-ups which followed produced distrust on the part of the pilots.

EARLY DEVELOPMENTS IN ENGLAND AND THE U.S.A.

In England the Frank Whittle turbo-jet engine underwent intensive tests in April 1937. After large-scale modifications and improvements in design the Whittle engine was installed in a Gloucester E-28 airplane specially built for the purpose.

Piloted by Sayers the Gloucester equipped with this engine first flew in May 1941. In October 1941 a group of Power Jet Company engineers took the engine and drawings to the United States to give the General Electric Co. technical assistance in developing turbo-jet engines. The first American flight took place a year later when a Bell Aircraft, the P-59, powered by two General Electric IA engines of Whittle type, flew successfully.

Utilizing the experience accumulated during the construction of their original aircraft the Gloucester Company designed and built a two-engine jet fighter, the Meteor, the only jet aircraft from the Allies that took part in World War II. It flew for the first time in March 1943. Meteors operated from airfields in South-East England against German buzz-bombs. On November 7, 1945, a specially-built Gloucester Meteor IV set up the world speed record of 969.6 k.p.h.

In 1945 the De Havilland Company started to develop a tailless jet aircraft, the DH-108, and built two machines, in one of which John Derry, a test pilot, set up in April 1948 the world speed record of 973.81 k.p.h., flying along a 100 km. closed loop. And in September in the same plane the same pilot diving from 36,000 feet down to 18,000 feet reached a speed of nearly 1,120 k.p.h., or practically the speed of sound.

However, both DH-108s came to grief shortly one after another, disintegrating in the air and killing two courageous fliers, John Derry and Captain Geoffrey De Havilland.

The reasons for the disasters lay in the fact that the designers had too little experience on which to base their calculations of airworthiness for such high-speed planes. Feelings of distrust towards jet-powered aircraft arose among our airmen, too, since the first flights in jet planes in our country also ended disastrously.

JET RESEARCH OF SOVIET DESIGNERS

In the Soviet Union many designers were engaged in practical work on jet engines during the initial stage, concentrating in the main on developing the liquid jet engine. Of considerable help were the works of A. F. Tsander, a scientist and designer, the follower of Tsiolkovsky, who as far back as 1930-33 made his first jet engines which at that time and much to our regret found no practical application. At the end of the 30s designers Isayev and Dushkin developed jet engines, which were installed in planes built specially for the purpose, and saw their creations in jet-powered flight.

The jet-engine designer A. Lyulka pioneered Soviet jet-power plants in the Soviet Union by building his first aircraft jet engine in 1937.

At the beginning of 1942 the test pilot Grigory Bakhchivanji was preparing to take up a jet plane designed by Bolkhovitinov and equipped with a liquid jet designed by Isayev and Dushkin for a test flight. Severe Siberian frosts set in and conditions were hardly suitable for test flights. But the final work of completing the machine and getting it ready for test flights did not cease even for a moment. There was a war on! The will and enthusiasm of the plane builders, engineers and the pilot helped to overcome all the hardships of severe conditions of war time and the lack of research facilities.

Finally the aircraft was completed and in May 1942 Bakhchivanji made his first flight in it to the loud applause of all present.

However, during one of the routine test flights when the pilot switched on full thrust, the airplane streaked like a meteor in the sky above the amazed people, lost stability, went out of control and hurtled to the ground at tremendous speed.

It was a heroic deed by the courageous test pilot and pioneer of jet aviation Grigory Bakhchivanji who gave his life to the mastering of flying technique of the first Soviet jet aircraft.

AGAIN IN THE KREMLIN

At the end of December 1945 the People's Commissar and I were summoned to the Kremlin. After discussing the work of the aircraft industry we considered as to whether it was expedient to put into mass production the captured German jet fighter Messerschmitt-262. In the course of the discussion Stalin, the Chairman of the State Council for Defence, asked me whether I knew this aircraft and what was my opinion of it.

"I have a general idea of jet-powered flight," I said. "I know the Me-262, but I think that it should not be put into mass production."

"Why so?"

"Because it's a bad plane, with a very complicated control system and poor stability. A number of crashes in Germany in this aircraft prove my point. If we adopt it in our Air Force it will scare our pilots away from jet aviation, because very soon they will learn from their own experience that the machine is dangerous to handle and its take-off and landing performance is poor. And, finally, if we start to copy the Messerschmitt aircraft all our attention and resources will be mobilized for the purpose and great damage will be done to the work on our Soviet jet planes."

WE MUST FIND OUR OWN WAY

I spoke against copying German planes since I thought their designs to a large extent raw and unsuccessful. At that time the Germans built better jet engines than ours but their planes were inferior.

Then they asked me: "How's the work on jet planes progressing with our designers?"

"Quite successfully. Very soon we shall fly, only you must give us all possible attention and support. Artem Mikoyan is working on a twin-engine fighter, the MiG-9 and we have built a single-engine Yak-15."

"When do you intend to fly?"

"The Yak-15 has made its first runs and short flights at the airfield. Now we shall take it to the Central Institute of Aerohydrodynamics, test it in a full scale wind-tunnel and then give it a first flight test. Mikoyan too promised to have his plane ready for flights by the spring."

"In what way will our planes be better than those of the Germans?"

"They'll be lighter, more reliable and simple to control, with better flying performance, and could be adopted for mass production much sooner."

"Suppose you fail in your promises?"

"We won't, you'll see it very soon."

"If you make your promise good, your machines will take part in the fly-past at Tushino," Stalin said.

That's how the question of the ways of development of jet-powered aviation was solved in our country.

ANOTHER VICTIM

Everyone of us was carried away by the novelty of the task. Our first work was to instal a liquid jet engine in a Yak-3 to improve its performance. But although the result was quite impressive—the speed of the airplane with the liquid jet engine switched on went up to 800 k.p.h.—Victor Rastorguyev, a well-known flier, who flight-tested the plane was dissatisfied with it.

Yak-15 jet fighter

Two-engined ten-seat passenger plane Yak-16

"Flying this plane is like kissing a tigress," he joked. "It's frightening and no pleasure at all."

True, there was no end to special pumps, nitric acid tanks, all sorts of valves and reductors installed in the aircraft which was entangled in a maze of pipings. The liquid jet engine was very unreliable in operation. We were just beginning to master the new field. Acid pipes leaked, noxious fumes evaporated. Mechanics went about in overalls full of holes, their hands burned by acid.

But the speed of the machine was very impressive. It was being prepared for a fly-past in which to our regret it did not take part. At one of the rehearsal flights Victor Rastorguyev met his end together with the plane.

Along with designers Adler and Shekhter, we thought matters over for a long time before deciding on a final version. All possible solutions had to be taken into account.

Yevgeny Adler was appointed leading designer —he was called upon to be the soul of the future aircraft. Both Adler and Shekhter were very capable designers who gained experience and matured at our plant. They came to the plant in the early 30s straight from their draughtsman's courses and, although lacking higher education, they won recognition through hard work and inborn talent for designing and eventually were entrusted with very responsible work in our designing bureau. Later on they graduated from the institute and received their diplomas without giving up their work as did many other of our designers.

THE YAK-15

Taking the general situation into consideration along with a certain feeling of wariness towards jet aviation due to a number of catastrophes we had in the West we thought it of prime importance to make pilots believe in jet planes, to make them realize that they were no more complicated to control and no more dangerous to fly in than a conventional piston-engine craft. Our idea was to take an ordinary piston-engine aircraft, introduce a new engine and make as few changes as possible. The pilot would then find himself in familiar surroundings and not notice the difference between jet and conventional planes when taking off or landing.

We managed to carry our idea into effect and, as the future showed, we did not err when we installed a jet engine in a Yak-3 fighter which was, of course, familiar to our pilots. We had to reshape the plane's nose section radically but the rest of the plane, cockpit, wings, tail-plane, landing gear, suffered no considerable changes.

According to our calculations, the plane was to be very light, simple to control and capable of over 800 k.p.h. which is far more than the speed of the serial Yak-3.

The designers and the workers were possessed by the desire to see their jet first-born in flight, and by the autumn of 1945 the machine was rolled out on to the airfield for its first engine tests, taxiing, runs and short flights. The plane made its first very brief flights close to the ground. Doubts assailed us: will the fuselage under plating hold out during a regular flight, will it resist the hot gases escaping from the exhaust nozzle just aft of the wing?

To eliminate these doubts we decided to test the plane with its engine running in the wind-tunnel of the Central Institute of Aerohydrodynamics.

It was a fantastic spectacle: the Yak-15 roaring away inside the wind-tunnel mounted on aerodynamic weights. The temperature at various points along the fuselage and the moments arising with the engine operating at different rates were taken. At the end of the experiment we saw that everything was all right and that the machine was ready to fly.

YOU'LL KILL ME!

The plane was brought to the airfield but rainy weather had turned the runway into a lake. We had to wait until the airfield dried up enough to take off. At last the time came for the first flight.

Calm and confident, Mikhail Ivanov, the test pilot, climbed into the cockpit saying that everything would be all right.

The engine was started and the unaccustomed ears of those present were deafened by the characteristic whine of a jet engine.

The engine was tested: everything was all right. After a short run Ivanov was airborne.

The first flight of our jet plane. Our hearts sang with joy.

The plane made its landing approach and landed smoothly. Mikhail had hardly had time to taxi to the starting-line and climb out of the cabin when dozens of hands tossed him high in the air. One, two, three....

"Whoa, boys, hold it! You'll kill me!" laughed the pilot.

His first impressions of the flight were: considerably less noise in the cabin and complete absence of the vibration usual with a piston engine. As regards control there was no difference between piston-engined and jet-powered planes. In short the first impression was favourable.

On the same day and at the same airfield Grinchik, another test pilot, made his first jet-powered flight in the Mikoyan and Gurevich MiG-9.

It was a double holiday for us.

The results of the test flights in the Yak-15 and MiG-9 were reported to Mikhail Khrunichev, the Minister of Aircraft Industry who was closely watching our progress in developing Soviet jet aviation. Together with Mikoyan we were given instructions to begin preparations for the Tushino fly-past.

To rule out any unexpected incidents during the fly-past over the holiday crowds at the airfield, each aircraft had to be put through a definite programme of flight tests.

Day after day, all through the summer Ivanov, Adler and other members of the test team pottered about the Yak-15. The first flights brought us, as we had expected, a few surprises. There was not a single day that Ivanov did not take the machine up in the air. All our thoughts and aspirations lay in the Yak-15 and each of us considered its successes his own.

Our tension mounted as the day of the fly-past drew nearer. Only Mikhail Ivanov was unruffled. He liked the plane more and more with every flight. After each scheduled flight he would invariably answer my anxious questioning with: "Everything's all right. Don't you worry. The plane is a real daisy. It'll ring the bell at the fly-past."

The tail skid-wheel caused us a lot of trouble:

it was in the jet exhaust stream and after each flight we found it burnt. Besides the fuselage under plating was scorched every time. Adler solved the problem of the skid-wheel very quickly and the underside of the fuselage was sheathed in heat-resistant stainless plate steel. There were no other serious faults. By August the plane was thoroughly tested and was admitted for the fly-past rehearsal at the Tushino Airfield.

At the dress rehearsal the Yak-15 made a very good impression and Ivanov was finally included on the programme of the air-show.

At last the day which we had awaited so long came. I could not sleep that night and I think Artem Mikoyan was also unable to sleep.

And as was usual in such cases, despite the fact that every single thing was checked and rechecked for the umpteenth time, I was seized with a strange and uncontrollable agitation the moment I stepped out on the flat roof of the Chkalov Central Aeroclub, where we, the designers of the planes that took part in the fly-past, usually received invitations to watch the show.

I thought I was the first to arrive but Artem Mikoyan was already there. We were in the same state of nervous expectation, experiencing the same feelings. We looked at each other and burst out laughing:

"Friends in need," I said.

"Or, perhaps, in luck," he joked. "We haven't got long to wait and learn."

Gradually the stands of the aeroclub were filled by the noisy and festive crowd eagerly waiting for the fly-past to begin. We exchanged greetings with our numerous acquaintances, smiled politely and no one even guessed how we felt.

The rim of the vast, emerald-green airfield
teemed with crowds of spectators. There was mer-
ry bustle everywhere: bands played forth, thousands of people milled round festively decorated
pavilions. Muscovites kept glancing at the sky impatient to see new aircraft and to admire the flying skill of our pilots. And as usual during this favourite people's holiday the organizers of the fly-
past, pilots and we, the designers, felt great respon-
sibility. Before each event the radio announcer briefly went over the stunts and gave the names of the pilot and of the designer of an aircraft.

A few minutes before the fly-past was due to begin, members of the Party and the Government appeared on the balcony amid cheers and applause. The fly-past began.

HAPPINESS

Yak-12s carrying the colours of the Soviet republics flew low over the stands to the solemn strains of the national anthem.

The gun salute boomed when a large group of Yak trainers appeared in the air followed by Glinka's "Glory" played by the band. Then air sportsmen, young men and women and Air Force pilots, performed exciting group and individual stunts. Mikoyan and I saw nothing and heard nothing. We were waiting for our jet firstlings to appear. At last came the coveted moment. The sky over the airfield cleared and we heard the announcer say that a jet aircraft designed by Yakovlev was approaching the airfield. True enough, a black dot was swiftly approaching the boundaries of the field at a low height Another moment, and I already recognized the familiar outlines. The Yak-15 piloted by Ivanov flashed past the stands with a whistle characteristic of jet planes; a MiG-9 followed it a few seconds later.

Everyone at the airfield broke out with stormy applause, expressing their joy and admiration. I was brimming with boundless genuine happiness. Dozens of people crowded round Mikoyan and me congratulating, hugging and kissing us. We stood there utterly exhausted feeling weak from the excitement.

Yak-18A, a two-seater for primary training

Two-engined jet fighter Yak

A thought flashed in my mind: how was Adler who had been at the plane's take-off and was now waiting for Ivanov's return? A warm friendly feeling rose in my heart towards that fine fellow-worker and enthusiast deeply in love with his work.

I was sure that most of our workers who had put a lot of effort and creative energy into the Yak-15 were full of excitement on that happy and notable day: Kirill Vigant, our erudite engineer, Sergei Kulagin and Boris Kerber, my assistants, Kostya Sinelshchikov, the oldest worker in our designing bureau, Viktor Shelepchikov, the oldest designer, Sergei Makarov, a man of vast knowledge and capabilities, shouldering all our calculations, Klavdia Kildisheva, the head of research and laboratory tests, Anatoly Bezborodov, the head and soul of the production, Alexander Voropanov, our plant Party secretary, Alexander Zhirov, head of the machine shop, Pavel Pozdnyakov and Mikhail Maximov, and many, many others.

Splendid people! I wished I could hug them all to share with them my happiness and pride for our wonderful well-knit body of workers.

The fly-past came to an end. People streamed out to their cars. My old driver Misha Sushchinsky brought me home in two winks. I dropped down in my bed and slept like dead until morning.

The next day after the show Mikoyan and I were summoned to the Kremlin. The conversation was very brief. We were congratulated upon our success and told the following: Artem Mikoyan and Deputy Minister Pyotr Dementyev were to start off immediately for one aircraft plant while I together with another Deputy Minister Alexander Kuznetsov was to leave for another plant. We were entrusted with the building and testing of a dozen jet planes Yak-15 and MiG-9 for the October holiday fly-past over the Red Square. We were told not to return to Moscow until we should have completed our tasks.

Two and a half months were all we had before the deadline and not a single drawing of any value to work on for the serial production plant. It seemed impossible to carry out the task. But they would not take "no" for an answer. "You'll have all the help necessary." We had no time to lose, and two or three days later a formidable group of designers and workers left for the plant.

Since there were no working drawings, and it would have taken months to make them we decided to start building the planes by experimental drawings used for our prototype Yak-15.

For several days running all the printing-shops

in the town were duplicating our drawings, twenty sets all in all, nearly 60 thousand copies.

At the same time our designers and workers began to pile up the material in the shops and made the necessary tools and appliances. We had to take great technical risk in many things. But it proved to be justified. And although we had to remake a thing or two later on, the economy of time was great.

PRACTICALLY A MIRACLE

Success lay in the conscientious approach of our plant and designing bureau workers. The people worked with enthusiasm I had never witnessed before. Our jet planes took shape with every day according to the strict schedule. It seemed there was no limit to the capabilities of men who knew their business well, were united in their efforts and firmly believed in their strength.

Every morning Alexander Kuznetsov held brief conferences to check on the shop's work schedules. No idle talk, only schedule was discussed. If the shop fell behind the schedule another emergency schedule was drawn up. To give an incentive to shop managers a system of bonuses was established for the fulfilment of daily schedules. If the schedule had not been kept to and one shop manager blamed another for failure, their explanations were disregarded and they both lost their bonuses. Progressive bonus system was introduced for the workers.

Four weeks elapsed and the first plane was wheeled out of the assembly shop. It was disassembled, packed in a special container and sent off to Moscow by an express train.

On October 5 the second plane appeared and sixteen days later we shipped our last Yak-15.

We would call it a miracle if we believed in them. But we believed in human hands and not in miracles. These skilful human hands attained what seemed to be impossible, they practically wrought a miracle.

PROPELLERLESS PLANES

At one of the Moscow airfields our planes and the MiG-9s which had been also completed by the time and brought for the trials were subjected to extensive flight tests.

The airfield presented an unusual sight in those days: planes unfamiliar in appearance, without propellers, were lined up at the runway edge. A swarm of mechanics and pilots, civilian and Air Force pottered around them.

There was little time left before the settled date November 7, and we had to flight-test and adjust all planes and to teach several dozen Air

Force pilots, participants of the fly-past, to fly them.

On the early morning of November 7, all planes were lined up at one of the airfields near Moscow with the pilots in the cockpits ready for the take-off.

All Air Force pilots had had their bit of training and each of them had made a number of flights in his plane. They had even flown a few times in formation.

Unfortunately, dense fog prevented our MiGs and Yaks from taking off that day and the entire fly-past was cancelled.

It was only on May 1, 1947 that the Muscovites saw for the first time Soviet jet fighters over the Red Square. But the months between the holidays were not wasted. Our aircraft plants produced scores of Yak-15 and MiG-9 jet fighters and flights in them became an ordinary thing for the Air Force pilots.

AIRMEN BELIEVED IN NEW PLANES

Airmen came round to trust jet airplanes and saw that it was not dangerous to fly in them.

In May 1947 the Yak-15 successfully passed state trials. It was the first Soviet jet plane to be adopted for operational service in the Air Force.

In the spring of 1947 another event marked a new stage in the development of jet aviation. General Pyotr Stefanovsky, a well-known test pilot, performed basic figures of aerobatics in a Yak-15.

In 1947 Ivan Polunin, an Air Force pilot, demonstrated aerobatics in a Yak-15 before the numerous spectators and foreign military attachés at the Tushino air-show.

Group flying in jet fighters led by the twice Hero of the Soviet Union Yevgeny Savitsky were shown for the first time during the fly-past in 1948.

Jet planes were inaugurated in our aviation through the efforts of engineers, workers of aircraft industry and our test pilots.

In 1948 the Presidium of the Supreme Soviet of the U.S.S.R. awarded the title of Hero of the Soviet Union to four test pilots who had highly distinguished themselves in mastering new jet planes: Pyotr Stefanovsky, Mikhail Ivanov, Ivan Fyodorov and Ivan Ivashchenko.

We were glad to hear the good news since we realized that by so doing the Supreme Soviet appreciated the merits not only of these particular pilots, but of all test and Air Force pilots who blazed the path in the 20th-century aviation.

THE NEW TASK

For the three decades of its existence our designing bureau developed mainly fighters and trainers. You can well imagine the surprise among aviation specialists in our country and abroad when the newspapers reported that our designing bureau developed a giant helicopter, the flying wagon.

The story of the flying wagon is somewhat unusual.

At the end of the summer of 1952 I was summoned to the Kremlin where I found Tupolev, Ilyushin and helicopter designers Mil, Kamov and Bratukhin. This strange combination of the invited designers surprised me since plane and helicopter people had very little in common and met rarely.

As soon as the conference began everything became clear. We were called in to discuss how to eliminate the gap in building large helicopters.

True enough, in those days we lagged behind the United States in that field. There were not enough designers working in helicopter building, we were told, and the Government decided to ask the leading aircraft designing bureaus to try their hand in a field somewhat unusual for them and to help in developing large helicopters.

TICKLISH JOB

Mikhail Mil who worked for many years in helicopter building was the only one who came to the conference with a ready suggestion based on the working drawings of a twelve-passenger helicopter which he had designed. For us aircraft builders the whole thing was rather unexpected.

Andrei Tupolev and Sergei Ilyushin said that they could not take part in designing helicopters since their bureaus had far too much work as it was, and since they had had no experience whatsoever in that field. When my turn came, I said that we, too, were hard pressed with work but we had some idea about the helicopter. In recent years we built two small experimental whirlbirds and if granted certain help we could launch the job of designing a large helicopter. I asked permission to consult my staff before giving the final answer. We were given one more day to consider the idea.

When I returned to the designing bureau, I summoned Nikolai Skrzhinsky who worked on helicopters way back in the 30s, Pyotr Samsonov, a veteran of aircraft building and a very experienced engineer, Leon Shekhter and Igor Erlich who had been the leading designer of our experimental helicopters. We had no time to lose since less than 24 hours were left to make up our minds.

"Flying wagon"

Four-seat aeromobile Yak-12A

I explained the matter in a nutshell, and we set to thinking: developing helicopters was rather a ticklish job. The difficulties which arose in large helicopter building in the U.S.A. and Britain came to our minds and, of course, we could not take our experience seriously. Developing small experimental craft was one thing and creating a giant passenger-cargo helicopter was quite another. But since the Government asked us and since it was not "the gods who cooked the pots" we decided to tackle the job of designing a 24-passenger twin-engine helicopter. After some consideration we calculated that it would take us one year to develop and prepare working drawings.

UNEXPECTED SUGGESTION

The next evening I was at the Kremlin again. Only Mil was there this time. The whole matter took a completely unexpected for us and especially for me turn.

We were told to look through the already prepared draft of the Government decision on building two helicopters and to give our comments. Mil's designing bureau was entrusted with the task of developing a single-engine one-rotor twelve-passenger helicopter while we had to build a twin-engine two-rotor 24-passenger helicopter. The most difficult part of the task was that we were given only one year to develop, build and test both helicopters.

The day before my assistants and I thought it impossible to develop a craft in less than one year, while now we were given one year for everything. It seemed to us that to solve this complicated problem would take minimum three to four years. We tried to argue the date, but were explained that helicopter building was in a very bad shape and the matter could not wait any longer. We would be given unlimited help and the fixed time of one year was final and was not to be debated. By and by, Mil was talked into consenting; I also had to give in.

On the following day the decision was signed. The fixed date put a scare into everyone who was to work on the helicopter and our "good-wishers" were already prophesying inevitable failure for us.

But before I proceed with the story let me tell you a few words about the history of the helicopter, so that you could realize the difficulties we were up against.

FOLLOWING IN LEONARDO DA VINCI'S STEPS

Leonardo da Vinci was the first who 450 years ago thought of building a helicopter—a craft hovering in the air with the help of a propeller rotating horizontally. From the sketch of Leonardo da Vinci's draught we may judge that his idea was quite sound.

In 1754 our great countryman Mikhail Lomonosov presented at the sitting of the Academy of Sciences his project of the aerodynamic machine for studying the upper layers of the atmosphere. Lomonosov built a model of his machine in which the propellers were rotated by a clock spring.

But a project or even a model is one thing and a flying helicopter is quite another.

It was only at the beginning of our century that man managed to rise up into the air in a rotor-driven machine—helicopter. Russia's first helicopter was built prior to the First World War in the Moscow Higher Technical School by the aeronautics group from a design made by Boris Yuryev, one of the students who later became an academician.

However, the war interrupted the work on helicopters which was resumed only after the Revolution.

In 1932 Professor Alexei Cheremukhin set a world altitude record of 605 metres in a helicopter developed at the Central Institute of Aerohydrodynamics.

In the 30-40s the designers Sikorsky (Russian by birth) and Piasecki in the United States and the Bristol Aircraft Company in Britain where helicopter designing was directed by Hafner, a well-known Austrian specialist, doggedly pushed on their research in helicopters.

For many years Piasecki was fighting a losing battle with vibration in his YH-16 helicopter. Hafner also spent quite a number of years to "cure" *Bristol* Type E-173 helicopter from the same "disease." Vibration was the most dreaded and hard to cure "disease" which developed in all helicopters. We were confronted with it as soon as our helicopter was designed, built and brought to the airfield to be flight-tested.

ZERO SPEED

Speed, speed and once more speed was the main target of the workers of our designing bureau. From plane to plane every year we strove to build up the speed. But it was not the speed that counted in a helicopter, it was rather its ability to hover motionlessly in the air at zero speed, to raise heavy cargo vertically.

We decided on an original twin-rotor, tandem design and were not to regret it later. It was more stable than a single-rotor design, lifted considerable load and what was more important, it had a roomy cargo compartment allowing to carry bulky cargo.

We had no experience in building helicopters of the chosen design and had to begin from scratch, making a series of complicated experiments to solve difficult research problems with the help of the scientific workers from the Central Institute of Aerohydrodynamics and the Central Institute of Aircraft Engine Building. The combination of our experience with profound scientific analyses prevented grave errors in the design of a helicopter and its assemblies. However, when the helicopter was built and underwent static engine tests it turned out that it was impossible to plan everything theoretically. Many new problems cropped up, the problem of engine cooling being one of them. The flying aircraft moves in a stream of air, and the engine is cooled intensively. In our case we had to make heavily loaded helicopter hover in the air and therefore its engine cooling had to be forced.

Vibration, however, was the main difficulty that caused us no end of trouble.

QUADS

The Ministry of Aircraft Industry closely followed our progress. Broad co-operation between various plants was organized, and the Ministry gave priority to all helicopter parts that were being built at various aircraft plants. The work proceeded at a rapid pace. Four helicopters were built simultaneously: one for laboratory static strength and stress tests, a second one for dynamic test at the airfield when endurance life of the engines and rotors of the captive helicopter hovering above the ground was determined, the third and fourth helicopters were intended for the plant and state flight tests.

Satisfactory results of the tests of one of the four helicopters did not exclude the possibility of failure when testing the remaining three. For example, the model slated for static tests could and sometimes did pass the complete test programme, while its brother failed to make the dynamic tests and had to be improved for years afterwards. The experience of the Americans and British spoke for itself.

Besides the above-mentioned tests conducted at our plant some of the helicopter assemblies were checked at other plants and research institutes.

Thus the rotor reductor, the most important assembly, was tested at the engine plant where it had been made; rotor blades were vibration-tested at the Central Institute of Aerohydrodynamics where, to prove their reliability they were subjected to a dozen million vibrations; the power plant, fuel and cooling systems were tested at the Aircraft Engine Research Institute. These tests were in the main successfully completed in due time.

The trouble began with the helicopter which underwent the endurance test. Vibration set in already after the very first hours of operation of the engine and rotors. The machine vibrated while operating at various rates and we could do nothing about it. As soon as we got the vibration under control in one place, it would invariably crop up somewhere else. And so it went on like in a fairy-tale: you pull out your nose and find your tail stuck in; you pull out your tail and lo, your nose is in the bog again. But the vibration was nothing compared with what awaited us.

Three-hundred-hour endurance test had to be made to check reliable operation of all helicopter parts before proceeding to test the captive helicopter hovering above the ground on mooring lines. We were impatient to run the helicopter through the required 300 hours of operation. The whole trouble with these tests was that in the event of a break-down of some kind we would have to begin from the very beginning. Every other hour of tests brought joy to us on the one hand and growing alarm on the other: what if there would be a break-down? After 150 hours of operation we got the better of the vibration. The coveted figure of 300 hours was drawing nearer. Our confidence in the success of the test mounted when one day an excited voice came over the telephone from the airfield: "There's been trouble. The helicopter disintegrated on the ground and is burning up. Nothing can be saved. The cause is unknown."—"What about the people?"—"They are all safe."

WE BEGIN FROM THE BEGINNING

I rushed to the airfield only to find a sad sight. The helicopter was reduced to a heap of charred rubble. Twisted rotor blades lay scattered all round. The machine went through 178 hours of operation and now we had to begin from the very beginning.

The emergency commission of well-known specialists located at long last with our help the cause of trouble. The culprits turned out to be the attachment units of the rear engine frame which had collapsed under the weariness stress. The rear engine with the reductor had lunged forward and the rotor blades began to chop the machine to pieces. Petrol had gushed forth from the severed pipelines onto the heated engine starting fire.

We all looked down in the mouth, for it was really hard to begin from the beginning.

I tried to console my assistants: we had been lucky to find the cause of trouble. It would be corrected. Besides the work we had done during those 178 hours of operation did not go to waste. After

Giant Tu-114 turbo-jet passenger plane—the fastest and the most roomy airliner in the world

Four-engined passenger liner Il-18

all that was what the endurance tests were for: to find such faults in good time.

But while consoling the others I myself was terribly upset. There was nothing for it but to begin the tests with double energy, the more so, because we had already put one of our helicopters to flight tests.

A crew of the test pilots Sergei Brovtsev and Yegor Milyutichev, flight engineers, mechanics and WT operators was appointed for the flight tests.

Brovtsev was an experienced helicopter test pilot, while Milyutichev, young and capable, was just beginning his career as a test pilot. Later this combination, Brovtsev-Milyutichev proved to be a very happy one.

VIBRATION

After their first timid flights Brovtsev and Milyutichev praised the helicopter mildly. They performed jumps, hops and hovered about thirty feet above the ground. The pilots carefully studied the machine trying to thoroughly fathom its performance.

The leading designers of the helicopter were present at all these test flights and we discussed the results together with pilots and designers at my office. We pushed ahead cautiously feeling the ground.

After hundreds of short flights, each lasting only

a few minutes, during which the engine operated at half its rated power, Brovtsev said that it was time to have a real go at it. We gave him the OK.

When Brovtsev and Milyutichev took their places in the pilots' cabin, opened for the first time full throttle, the engines roared mightily and the rotor blades hurling aside powerful backwash lifted the helicopter and it gained height and picked up speed, all of us who were present at the first flight of the gigantic machine stood spellbound.

While working hard on the helicopter we, the designers, workers and pilots, realized that in the end it would fly, but when it actually flew there was no end to our joy.

After fifteen minutes of flight the pilots brought the helicopter down and we gave them a toss in the air and cracked a traditional bottle of champagne.

However soon afterwards both pilots somewhat embarrassedly and uncertainly mentioned "a tiny bit of vibration" appearing at certain flight attitudes.

FIVE MONTHS

Special, very sensitive vibration recording instruments were installed in the helicopter only to discover that true enough, at certain flight attitudes there appeared not the "tiny bit of vibration" as the pilots who did not want to disappoint the designers had delicately put it, but a real formidable vibration that made the whole frame of the helicopter shake dangerously.

For five solid months we tried to get rid of that vibration. Five months of intensive research, calculations, dozens of experimental flights—all in vain.

Here we must take into account one of the differences of a helicopter from a plane. In the plane all moving and rotating parts are concentrated in the engine, and vibration is absorbed by special shock-absorbers. In a helicopter anything can be the cause of vibration. One of the engines vibrates, the other engine vibrates, reductor vibrates, synchronous transmission coupling between two rotors also vibrates. It took us a long time to locate the primary cause of the vibration. Several months of wrestling with vibration in the helicopter reduced us to a condition of utter despair and even hopelessness. We began to lose every vestige of hope that we could ever eliminate the hated vibration, because it would suddenly appear in the most unexpected places. The time came when upon meeting each other in the morning we cried in place of a greeting: "Well, still vibrates?"—"It sure does!"—"Won't it ever stop!"

From the very beginning Shishkin who was responsible for the final stage of the helicopter testing secured efficient help from the Central Institute of Aerohydrodynamics and other research institutes. Upon my request A. Makarevsky, head of the Central Institute, called together all those who could be of any help in discussing the sum of problems connected with vibration. It was a very peculiar conference. Makarevsky, a prominent specialist in the field of aircraft frame stresses, Ananyev, the chief of the stress and vibration laboratory, scientific workers Zherebtsov, Vildgrube and some others persistently and doggedly sought the shortest way to overcome the dangerous and difficult "disease" of our helicopter. But there were scientists who bent their scientific learning and technical knowledge to find and present the most convincing proof that the vibration was inevitable, that, generally speaking, we were trying to cure an incurable "disease." One of them, a very reputed scientist, very imposing in appearance, brought diagrams and expertly juggling scientific terminology, formulae and figures tried to prove that we would not be able to get rid of vibration and that it was the organic shortcoming of our helicopter design.

There were many hypotheses and suggestions what to do and how to "cure" the vibration. Some suggested that the helicopter be made longer, others—shorter, still others suggested to redesign the fuselage. There were some who considered that all our efforts were in vain and advanced an argument: the Americans failed to get rid of vibration in a YH-16 helicopter, Hafner was still wrestling with the same problem in his *Bristol* Type-173. You think you are smarter than anyone else. Don't waste time. . . .

TORTURE

We were not wasting time. If we were soft-spined or if we blindly believed in theory without proving it by experiments and if we did not analyze the deductions of the scientists by engineering experience, it might be that we would not have had the helicopter even to this day. Fortified by the belief in our experience and helped by such scientists as Ananyev, Vildgrube, Zherebtsov we, at long last, found the correct engineering solution. This is how it happened.

Tormenting and racking my brains over the primary cause of vibration I arrived at the conclusion that it should be dealt with by stages.

I use the word "tormenting" because the idea really tormented me day and night, at the theatre, during my walks and at dinner-table. My mind would be distracted for a while but then the thought of the vibration would return hitting my brain with a new force. I would actually sweat all over from the feeling of impotence before the insurmountable obstacle that was facing us. One day we were struck by the idea that of all sources of vibration blades were the most probable one. The helicopter has four blades in each rotor or eight blades altogether. They rotate at a terrific speed giving rise to very complicated mechanical and aerodynamic moments.

What if we changed the blade vibro-characteristics? To convince ourselves that the blades were really the cause of vibration I suggested to try and chop off half a metre from each blade-tip, and then see how it would affect the vibration of the entire helicopter.

SURPRISE

Skrzhinsky, Erlich and others gathered once again, thoroughly discussed my suggestion and decided to give it a try.

Two weeks later new blades fifty cm. shorter were reinstalled in the helicopter. Then came the moment of suspense. The engines were started, blades whirled, Brovtsev signalled from the cabin: "All set." And the helicopter went up.

Brovtsev and Milyutichev stayed in the air for twenty minutes. We did not know how the helicopter had behaved up there, but we could see by the smiling faces of the pilots when they hovered low above the ground that we had scored bull's eye.

You can well imagine our satisfaction when Brovtsev and Milyutichev said that during their twenty-minute flight they had run the rotors at various operational rates and tested the helicopter in every flight attitude, but there was not a trace of vibration. It was one of those pleasant surprises which sometimes fortunately prove the advantage of the sound engineering reasoning over the philosophizing and scientific scholasticism. During the following tests we detected and corrected many various faults, but the vibration was the main one, and we had dealt with it nicely.

NEW TROUBLE

At the outset of the winter 1953 the helicopter was delivered for state trials. Everything seemed to be going smoothly, but fate had one more blow in store for us. Air Force pilots made hardly more than a dozen flights at the state trials, when during one of the static tests with the helicopter engine working at full power and only a mechanic present in the pilot's cabin, one of the mooring guys snapped, then a second one, a third and the last one. The helicopter soared and the mechanic who could not control it did the only right thing: he cut off the throttle. The helicopter had only gained about eight metres; it tilted sideways and crashed to the ground. There were no casualties, but the helicopter was completely demolished.

It was terrible. Failures brought depression and made some of the weak-spirited engineers turn their backs on our helicopter. Luckily, the main bunch of engineers, Skrzhinsky, Erlich, Bemov, Ogarkov, Brylin held fast.

The second model of the helicopter was ready for flight-testing and we turned it over to continue the state static tests. This time mooring guys were fortified.

But even when we brought our helicopter to the research and testing institute our troubles did not end. Perhaps it was because we wrestled with the vibration for so long or perhaps because one of our helicopters disintegrated and burned down and the first flight-test model crashed to the ground after breaking loose from its mooring.

CONVERSATION IN THE HELICOPTER

One day new planes including our helicopter were lined up for inspection by the top ranking officials of the Ministry of Defence at one of the airfields near Moscow. It was freezing hard.

The generals arrived and inspected the line of fighters and bombers. At last they came to the helicopter. They were glad to climb inside its huge cabin to escape the piercing wind. Altogether there were twenty people inside.

The Marshal turned to one of the top aviation officers: "Well, how's the helicopter? How are the trials coming along?"—"They spend more time repairing the machine than flying it. It is far from finished. The designer will have to work hard on it yet. The list of faults—"

The Marshal cut him short: "Enough of your red tape. Any machine can be buried under the lists of faults. We need a helicopter and not just a list of faults. Bear that in mind. Can this helicopter be approved or not, that's what must be determined. And as to the list of faults, settle that with the designer. Remember this is a new, unique flying machine."

IT BECAME EASIER TO BREATHE

After another two months of intensive testing the programme was completed. Institute test pilots Brovtsev, Shishov, Kravchenko, Tayursky and engineers Zagordan and Atabekyan spared no effort in testing the helicopter and helping us to eliminate all the faults. At last the helicopter was fully tested, approved and put by the Government's decision into mass production under the name of Yak-24.

We continued to work on the machine after it was already in the production-line stage, improving, for example, its controls.

It was the last serious modification after which we breathed more freely. The weight was off our shoulders completely when in 1955 four of our helicopters made their first public appearance to the delight of the numerous spectators.

Now a few words about the helicopter itself.

A TOUR OF THE HELICOPTER

The Yak-24 cabin resembles a metro or an electric train carriage. Truly, it is a real carriage ten metres long and about two metres in width and height. It can carry nearly forty passengers or close to four tons of various cargo including large dimension cargo, for instance, two motor cars which can drive up the ramp in the fuselage tail section.

The spacious pilot's cabin in the helicopter's nose section provides perfect observation. As from a balcony you can see everything around and even below you. The crew of two pilots, a flight engineer and a WT operator are provided with first-rate facilities: dual controls and numerous control instruments mounted in the panel in front of the pilot.

What are the basic advantages of the Yak-24 as compared to other helicopters of the same type?

Stability and controlability of the helicopter, payload and horizontal flight speed are the main features which any designer tries to combine in his machine.

In our helicopter we managed to sharply increase its payload capacity without cutting down on its speed. That is the main advantage of the Yak-24.

For the first time in the U.S.S.R. the main rotors were arranged in a tandem. Two huge four-blade rotors are situated in the nose and tail sections of the fuselage and rotate in opposite directions. The rotors are powered by two aircraft engines employing inter-connecting shafts. If one of the engines conks out, the other one will drive both rotors and the helicopter will continue to fly.

The rotors rotating horizontally above the fuselage lift the helicopter off the ground and raise it up into the air. Now, how does the helicopter attain level flight?

By manipulating the cyclic stick or the foot paddle the pilot changes the pitch of the main rotor blades tilting the tip-path plane forward, backward or sideways. When the two rotors are tilted simultaneously to one side, the helicopter flies horizontally in the required direction, and can be turned round by tilting the rotors in the opposite direction.

HELICOPTER'S PERFORMANCE

What is the flight performance of the helicopter? Milyutichev lifted four tons of cargo to 2,902 metres and Tinyakov took two tons of cargo up to 5,082 metres, demonstrating the helicopter's ceiling and payload capacity. Their achievements were approved by the International Aviation Federation as world records in 1956. In 1957 load capacity records were bettered by a new gigantic Soviet helicopter Mi-6.

Many non-stop flights initiated by the pilot Garnayev, Moscow-Leningrad one of them, demonstrated the endurance and range of the Yak-24. Modern navigational aids help the pilot to fly the helicopter at night and in bad weather.

In conclusion I want to specify that a helicopter and a plane are not rivals. Their purpose and utilization are different. As the plane advances in its development attaining greater speeds and load capacities it becomes more and more "attached" to the ground: requiring longer and sturdier runways which cannot be always built everywhere.

Any clearing slightly bigger than the size of the

Yak-24 is a satisfactory spot for it to land on or take off from. It can carry people and cargo to places inaccessible for trains and motor cars. In the rigid conditions of the Arctic, in the mountainous regions, in the vast forbidding taiga the helicopter is indispensable doing the work impossible for any other vehicle.

COLLECTIVE EFFORT

To be an aircraft designer is not enough to have the flare for designing or just be interested in technology from your childhood. Perfect knowledge of mathematics, physics and engineering is also insufficient. Designing, I would say, is not all science and technology, it is also an art, because creative process is inherent in it.

You come across the products of designing thought everywhere in our everyday life. Designing of modern machines, be it a plane, or a walking excavator, or even such insignificant as it may seem things as a bicycle and an electric iron or any other home appliance is a real creative process. It differs from the creative work of, say, a painter or of a writer in one thing: the designer, besides being the master of his knowledge with broad mental outlook and, of course, natural abilities, should also be a technologist, that is, he must know the most advantageous ways of putting his design into production, should be an efficient organizer and see his idea through at all the stages of the designing, building and testing.

No matter how original and brilliant the idea of a designer is, for its practical application it should be enriched by the creative effort of a great number of people—engineers and workers. Therefore, if the creative work of an artist, a composer or a writer is individual the work of a contemporary designer is truly collective.

IT IS A MUST FOR A DESIGNER

He must be thrifty in his designing work, spend materials without wasting, just enough to satisfy the requirement of usefulness, durability and reasonable attractiveness in designing home appliances.

The designer must strive for the simplicity of his design, a thing very hard to attain, so that the production of an aircraft required minimum labour.

The designer should foster in himself firmness, will-power, the ability to overcome difficulties and obstacles, patience and I would even say long suffering.

He must beware of complacency and conceit. Conceit is the death of a designer and especially of a creator of combat aircraft. The battle of military designers in peace time is no less intense than during war.

The designer should also be a dreamer because it is in his dreams that new ideas, new designes and ways of their implementation take shape. To carry the dream into reality is the highest purport of life of the man and of the designer especially.

NAÏVE FEARS

I remember the naïve fears of my youth days when it seemed to me that the adults had already invented and created everything. Locomotives and internal combustion engines had been built long before. Men had learned to produce electric energy and invented radio. Motor cars rolled along the roads and planes criss-crossed the sky.

However, the very first steps in my practical activity proved that I was wrong. Progress in technology is boundless. I learned that one solved task presented a host of new more complicated ones.

When I built my first glider I was seized by a powerful desire to design an aircraft. Then I wanted to make another one, a better one, then a third. When I worked on a plane there was only one thought gnawing at my mind: "If it only took off. That's all I want." Then the plane was finished and took to wing and I already began to think of creating a new, better and faster plane.

When a fast fighter was adopted as an operational aircraft in the Air Force, given the name of

Yak by a Government decision and put into mass production, it seemed that my dream had come true. But then a new dream would take shape in my mind.

To set yourself an aim, solve riddles, make experiments and in the end to score victory gives the designer great satisfaction. I am sure that this feeling is known to a designer.

The more difficult the goal is the greater will be the feeling of satisfaction when it is achieved.

COMING OUT OF SPIN

At the beginning of 30s when we were developing the UT-2 trainer aviation was fighting one of its most dangerous diseases—the spin.

Today everyone will tell you that the spin is a basic aerobatic stunt when the plane, seemingly uncontrolled, rapidly loses height rotating vertically about its longitudinal axis. A turn, then another, a third, then the pilot takes over and manipulating the control surfaces brings the plane out of the spin.

In those days things were different. The planes readily slipped into the spin and came out of it with great difficulty or not at all. Pilots lived in perpetual fear of the spin and it seemed to be lying in wait for them, taking advantage of the slightest mistake to wrench the machine from their hands. More often than not the plane would slip into the spin while the pilot was making a turn or a steep bank. The wing lift increased with the increase of the angle of attack. But the latter could be increased only to a very limited extent. Give the plane too much of a nose-up and instead of a streamline flow around the wing an air vortex will develop sharply reducing the wing lift. That's where the spin takes over paralizing the controls and making the plane uncontrollable.

The spin took heavy toll in the history of aviation in all countries, especially when parachute was just finding its way into aviation. Everyone rose up in arms against the spin. Scientists tested aircraft models in wind-tunnels trying to find ways of combating the spin. Hero pilots took the planes up into the air and observed the dangerous phenomenon at all its stages at the risk of their lives, to fathom why the planes became uncontrollable. Nature had to yield the secret.

It was found that the spin could be fought effectively by shifting the plane's centre of gravity forward and by increasing the effectiveness of the fin. After certain modifications the UT-2 trainer possessed perfect spin characteristics. This plane was later modified and made into a Yak-18, a first-year trainer. Pilots in the U.S.S.R. and in People's

Democracies get their training and receive pilot licenses in these planes. They jokingly call it "a flying desk." Today the once formidable spin is just another figure in any basic training programme.

HEAT BARRIER

After the speed of the planes surged past a 600 k.p.h. mark and climbed upwards, the aircraft builders were confronted with a new entirely unexpected phenomenon. The frame of the plane and especially its wings and tail-planes developed considerable vibration which sometimes became so intensive that the planes disintegrated in mid air. This phenomenon was called flutter.

When we conquered the spin in 1934 we thought that it would be smooth sailing from now on. Then came the problem of flutter, and again we thought: this was the last obstacle for the designers.

We were back at the laboratories making numberless tests. Test pilots wrestled with the flutter in the air until we found what caused it and elaborated counter measures.

New difficulties faced us when we approached the borders of the speed of sound.

To fly with the speed of more than one thousand kilometres an hour, to fly with the speed of sound! The idea seemed fantastic not so very long ago.

But life has made its corrections. Today we have planes flying with speeds far greater than the speed of sound, and we are not content with the results either. Supersonic speeds came after we conquered the so-called sonic barrier.

At supersonic speed the plane's drag sharply increases. The wing cuts through the air so swiftly that a compressed wave, the so-called shock-wave forms at its leading edge. The scientists had to revise old aerodynamic principles to change the shape of the plane's body and to use sweep-back wings which develop less drag instead of the conventional rectangular or trapezium-shaped wings.

This obstacle which gave us much trouble was overcome too. And once more a new surprise awaited us on our road to greater speeds—thermal barrier. At very high speeds the plane's surface becomes heated due to its friction with air particles. This problem is being successfully tackled today.

WE OVERCAME MANY OTHER BARRIERS

Aviation has long ago ceased to be the sole business of airmen alone. All branches of science and industry joined in the assault on speed and altitude.

The success of creating a new supersonic aircraft depends almost to an equal degree on the skill of designers and on metal-workers developing new light heat-resisting alloys; on the aerodynamic people and on the inventors of new plastics which find their way into aviation more and more. Aircraft building demanded that rivets be replaced by glue and the chemistry specialists had to work hard developing synthetic glue which had to be tougher than metal.

So unusual and difficult became the present-day flight conditions that not a single part, assembly or system is installed in the plane before it goes through a tremendous amount of tests, X-raying and special flight-simulating tests.

Take the plane's system of controls. How will it behave at supersonic speeds? The required stick and pedal force is so great that the pilot would be unable to control the aircraft with conventional system of controls. Supersonic aircraft employs powerful hydraulic boosters operating on special hydraulic fluid. What will happen to it when the plane zooms upwards from the ground temperature of 30°C into a 60°C cold way up in the sky in a matter of only a few minutes? It may toughen or freeze jamming the controls and then disaster is inevitable. The chemistry specialists went on searching and experimenting until they found the right fluid which was afraid of neither intensive heat nor severe cold.

Modern jet engines are very unpretentious as regards fuel and operate on ordinary kerosene. However at a great height where air is rarefied to a considerable degree kerosene begins to boil. Fuel tanks had to be provided with their own microclimate, that is, the necessary pressure had to be artificially maintained in them.

There is no end to such problems.

THIS IS NO LIMIT

To create new planes, to see how your ideas are transformed into ready parts, to see how out of these parts a plane gradually emerges taking the shape so familiar from your dreams and then watch your plane zooming upwards in the hands of a test pilot and to realize that thousands of such planes guard the skies of your country is the real happiness of creative work.

No matter what the difficulties and temporary failures of a designer, no matter how elusive the solution of the problem, final success crowns everything.

I remember our joy way back in 1930 when the first Soviet fighter we had developed was capable of a mere 250 k.p.h. Our achievement seemed tremendous in those days.

Only thirty years went by and our planes fly with speeds ten times greater and we are proud of it.

Is it the limit? How can we speak of any limits when the designers have solved most complicated problems of flight of guided and ballistic rockets. Small anti-aircraft missiles and the rockets which can reach into outer space dozens of thousands of kilometres away are the reality today.

Artificial earth satellites heralded the age of interplanetary travel. And now the perspective of flying to the Moon or even to Mars is no longer a mere freak of fantasy. New unexplored problems await scientists, engineers and designers in this field. We must work hard to conquer them, to reach deeper and deeper into the unknown, to realize our spectacular aims.

TO THE READER

The Foreign Languages Publishing House would be glad to have your opinion of the translation and the design of this book.

Please send all suggestions to 21, Zubovsky Boulevard, Moscow, U.S.S.R.

Printed in the Union of Soviet Socialist Republics

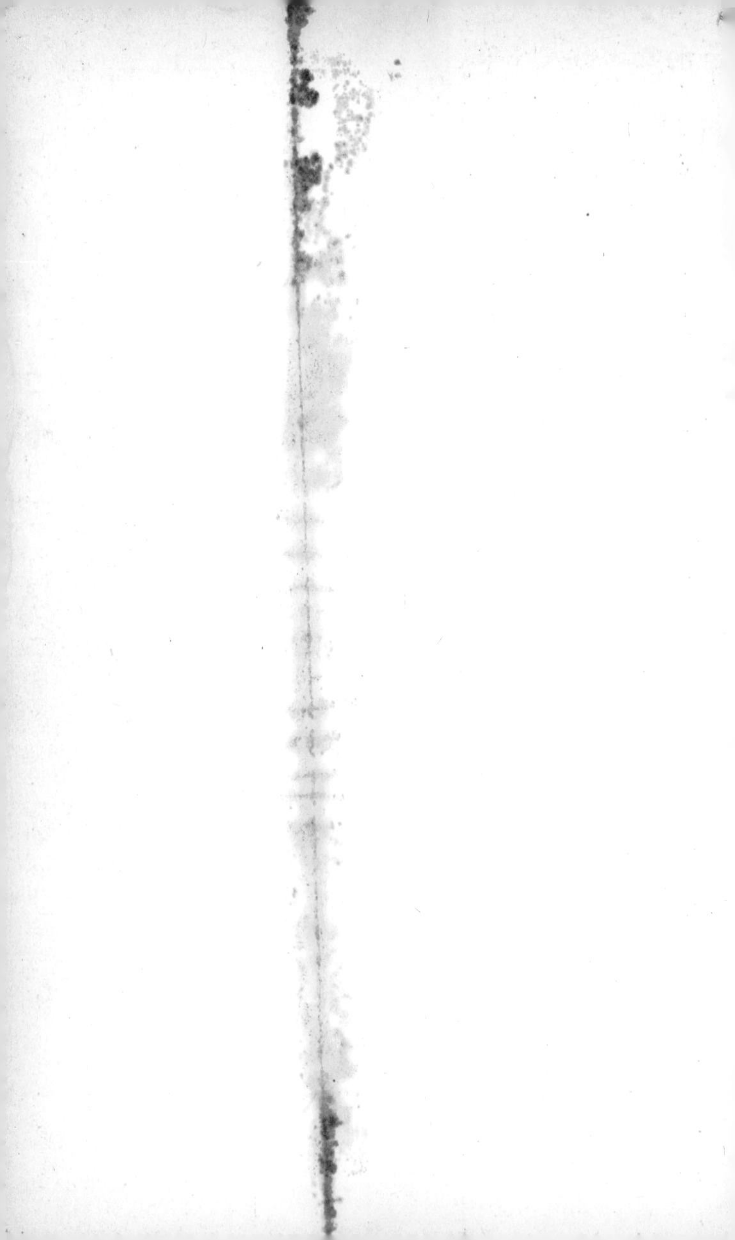